PRAISE FOR CATHRYN CONSTABLE

'A thrilling and atmospheric adventure, laced with magic.'
THE BOOKSELLER

'... [a] richness of setting and old-fashioned sense of adventure.'
THE SUNDAY TIMES

'*The Wolf Princess*, set in Russia, is a highlight of this year's fiction.'
THE TIMES

'Constable's passion for Russia comes across vividly; she
knows you have only to give reality a slight push to
make it marvellous. A classic winter's tale.'
FINANCIAL TIMES

'... an engrossing, deeply atmospheric story.'
THE DAILY TELEGRAPH

'There is something of Eva Ibbotson's magical storytelling
about *The Wolf Princess* by Cathryn Constable.'
THE SUNDAY TELEGRAPH

'This story is exciting, heart-warming and totally satisfying. Curl
up with Cathryn, jump on that unexpected train and steam
through the snow – wolves and a magical palace await you.'
LOVEREADING4KIDS

'*The Wolf Princess* is an enchanting and magical story, in the style
of classic children's book authors such as Eva Ibbotson.'
BOOKTRUST

A MESSAGE FROM CHICKEN HOUSE

Have you ever dreamt about the wind carrying you away, far out to sea, the wild waves sweeping you further and further into the cold north? Cathryn Constable's brilliant new story will do just that. In these pages, you'll discover a mystery both above and below the ocean's surface, a tale of shipwrecks, sea creatures and tangled trust. Here, a girl seeks the truth about her family and the dreadful threats to those she loves. It's a thriller, an adventure and a romance of wild imagination. Sail away – find yourself!

BARRY CUNNINGHAM
Publisher
Chicken House

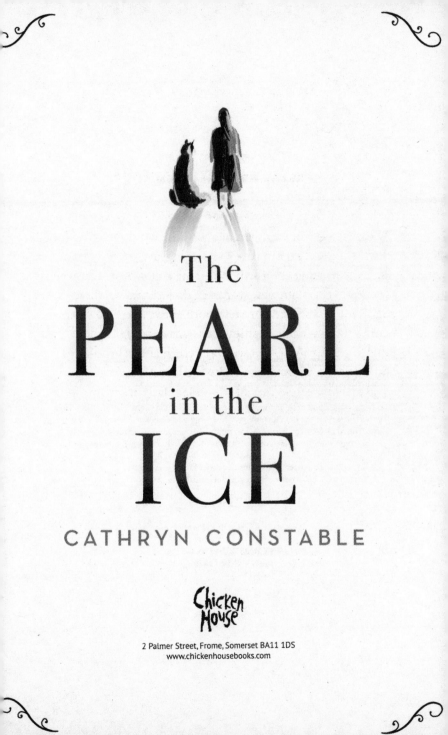

The
PEARL
in the
ICE

CATHRYN CONSTABLE

Chicken House

2 Palmer Street, Frome, Somerset BA11 1DS
www.chickenhousebooks.com

Text © Cathryn Constable 2019

First published in Great Britain in 2019
Chicken House
2 Palmer Street
Frome, Somerset BA11 1DS
United Kingdom
www.chickenhousebooks.com

Cover and interior design by Helen Crawford-White
Typeset by Dorchester Typesetting Group Ltd
Printed and bound in Great Britain by CPI Group (UK) Ltd, Croydon CR0 4YY

Lines from 'maggie and milly and molly and may' by E. E. Cummings © 1956, 1984, 1991,
by the Trustees for the E. E. Cummings Trust, from *The Complete Poems 1904–1962*
edited by George J. Firmage (Liveright, 1994) are used by permission of
Liveright Publishing Corporation, a division of W. W. Norton & Company.

The paper used in this Chicken House book is made
from wood grown in sustainable forests.

1 3 5 7 9 10 8 6 4 2

British Library Cataloguing in Publication data available.

PB ISBN 978-1-912626-51-9
eISBN 978-1-912626-63-2

C, M, R, S

Also by Cathryn Constable

The Wolf Princess

The White Tower

for whatever we lose (like a you or a me)
it's always ourselves that we find in the sea

E. E. CUMMINGS,
'MAGGIE AND MILLY AND MOLLY AND MAY'

But a mermaid has no tears,
therefore she suffers so much more.

HANS CHRISTIAN ANDERSEN,
'THE LITTLE MERMAID'

The great depths of the ocean are entirely unknown
to us. What passes in those remote depths – what beings
live, or can live, twelve or fifteen miles beneath the
surface of the waters – what is the organization
of these animals, we can scarcely conjecture.

JULES VERNE,
TWENTY THOUSAND LEAGUES UNDER THE SEA

1

Torn nail, gashed shin, ragged breath.

Marina Denham, twelve years old and slight for her age, hung from the branch of a London plane tree in the garden of her father's house in Hampstead.

She looked up at the blue sky through the lace of green leaves; one of the new airships of the king's fleet floated slowly above her, serene and silent as a cloud. What would it be like, she thought, to be the pilot of that cloudship, sedately patrolling the skies over the rooftops of London?

When I am grown, she thought, *and no one can tell*

3

me what to do, I will keep the sky safe for the king! I will be so brave that if an enemy bullet tore a hole in the skin of the ship, I'd climb out and fix it myself.

The dry, stale air of a London summer rustled through the tree. Who was she fooling? She knew she wasn't one for floating in those large, slow airships. 'Perhaps I'll go to sea instead . . .' She called up an image of herself as a battleship commander being saluted by her men, as a shrill bosun's whistle was caught by the brisk sea air . . . She liked the idea of being on a boat. All Denhams were good on boats, apparently. Although she had never been on one; had never seen the sea. Couldn't even swim.

'Got stuck, Denham?' jeered the boy in the tree next door, a copper beech. 'Why not give in?'

Her thoughts were quickly capsized.

Marina pushed her leg over the branch and then levered her body upwards, hidden once more amongst the leaves. Hand out, feel for the broken stump, swing to a sitting position and then slowly stand up to edge along the branch towards the trunk. This part, near the top of the tree, was always tricky. The danger was that you could be too confident and miss your footing. Or too desperate for victory and slip at the last moment.

The boy's blond head emerged from the leaves. *Now*

she would surprise him!

'What took you so long?' she asked.

'But – when?' His dirt-streaked face scrunched up in puzzlement. 'How did you . . . ?' He looked down. 'Impossible.' He shook his head and blew his hair out of his eyes. 'I swear, you would have been burned as a witch in—'

'Days of old,' she interrupted. 'Sadly for you, there was no witchcraft involved. Just skill. You were beaten fair and square, Edward Mount. No spells required.'

'Even so –' Edward lowered himself to sit on the branch as if he were riding a pony – 'I don't understand how you beat me every single time.'

'That's because the female is the superior gender of the species.'

'Hah! You wish!'

They sat in friendly silence for a while, staring at the backs of their houses through a veil of shivering late-summer leaves. One of the bedroom windows of Edward's house had the curtains firmly drawn, even though it was hours until dusk. Edward's mother was meant to have a baby any day now. The shutters on the library window of Marina's house were shut, too. But they had been shut for months, ever since her father had accepted the command of the HMS *Neptune* and

5

had locked himself away to prepare for the journey. Today he was leaving for the coast. In an hour. Perhaps less. And even though he had spent most of the last seven years at sea, so she should have got used to being alone, Marina felt the tug of a sad, lonely sort of sickness.

'Are you packed?' Edward said.

'Don't let's talk about it.' She pulled a leaf from the plane tree. It was as broad as her hand. She rolled it up and put it in her mouth as if it were a cigar. She must look awfully smart with her head tilted back against the trunk of the tree and her legs in their sailcloth trousers stretched out along the branch. She must look just like the illustration of the 'new woman' in Ivy's *Society News*.

'The *new woman* wears satin pantaloons and a turban. She neglects the pianoforte to smoke cigarettes of Turkish tobacco and rings her soulful eyes with *kohl*. The *new woman* is mistress of her own destiny. When she speaks, the world listens.' (How that last sentence made the hairs on the back of Marina's neck stand on end. She found it hard to make anyone, even Ivy, their housekeeper, listen to her.)

Marina turned to see if Edward could see her looking so very *new*, lost her balance and nearly toppled into the froth of green leaves below.

'You'll be forced to wear a skirt,' he added. 'No more

dressing like a boy.'

Trust Edward to puncture her plump, inflated dream. 'I wish I didn't have to go.'

'Have you spoken to your father?'

Marina chewed her lip. All these dreams of being a 'new woman' who could speak up for herself dissolved when she spoke to her father. When he looked at her, his small intelligent eyes focused intently, his quick mind already formulating a reply; it was as if he had the power to steal her voice.

'He's been too busy getting ready for his command,' she mumbled. 'He locks himself away in the library. Ivy has to leave his meals on a tray outside the door.'

'Understandable,' Edward reasoned. 'It's a big job, commanding a battleship. And the new class of dreadnought at that.' And under his breath, with great admiration, he whispered, 'All those *guns*.'

Marina didn't share Edward's fascination with gun turrets and bore sizes and how many shells could be launched in a minute, so she always ignored him when he started on about them.

'When's your father leaving?'

'Six o'clock for the train to Portsmouth.' Marina felt her chest get tight. Everything was changing. 'The *Neptune* sails tomorrow.'

'It won't be *all* bad,' Edward said. 'At your new school.'

'Easy for you to say! You get to go to a school with lessons in a forest and . . . and . . . boys and girls are treated the same. And you'll do painting and sculpture and . . .'

'But you'll have a lovely time doing embroidery!' He laughed. 'And French composition. Although how anyone thinks it's possible to turn *you* into a lady . . .' He snorted as he waved at her legs in their navy trousers. 'Hell will freeze over first.'

'I'll run away,' she whispered. She had never said this out loud, although she had thought it many times.

'Bit extreme,' Edward replied, unfazed. His sensible, easy nature was the thing that Marina most liked about him. She found that she was always interested in and usually surprised by his views, even if they were very different from her own. (Apart from when he wittered on about the guns on dreadnoughts.) Neither of them tried to convince the other of something: they simply enjoyed each other's company without question.

'Could you write to your mother?' he offered. 'Ask for her help?'

'I wouldn't know where to send the letter.' Marina swallowed.

'She won't come back?'

'It's been too long.' Marina shrugged. 'She left when I was small. You know this – I've told you.'

After a thoughtful silence, Edward said, 'Maybe she went home. Have you ever thought about that? My mother did. After the baby before last. She said we were all too noisy and spoilt and she couldn't think straight. She didn't come back for . . . for . . .' He squinted as he tried to remember. 'It was a long time, anyway. When she did finally come home, Maudie cried and told her that all we'd had to eat was cold sago pudding. Which was true. Father can't cook and Cook had given her notice and gone to work for the Stanleys. And then Mother cried. Even Father got his handkerchief out and blew his nose.' He shook his head. 'Barmy.'

'My mother won't come back now,' Marina said, trying to sound as if she didn't care. 'It's been too long.' Another thought. 'I've grown so much, she wouldn't recognize me even if she did.'

'Bad luck,' Edward said, and she was grateful for his sensitive reply. She knew that being the sort of boy he was – straightforward, helpful and decent – he wouldn't bring up the subject again.

'Even so, I wish my father wouldn't go away. I wish he wouldn't send me to that wretched Ladies' College.'

'What can't be cured must be endured.'

'You're not a vicar, so you can stop preaching.' She swung her leg over the branch to try and kick him. Pointless as he was too far away, but she needed to show him how annoyed she was.

'Marina! Marinaaaaaa!' She jumped in surprise at the sound of her father's voice, bellowing from the house.

'My father's leaving.' She threw herself into the dancing sea of green and gold leaves.

'Don't worry, Marina.' Edward's voice followed her. 'School can't possibly be as bad as you imagine. Nothing ever is.'

2

'Marina!'

She chased her father's voice through the scullery and up the stairs. The old house, with its broad floorboards and panelled walls taken from ships captained by long-dead Denhams, creaked appreciatively under her quick, light steps.

'Where have you been? I've been calling for you.' Her father stood in the hall, his old blue kitbag at his feet, looking at one of the sea charts on the wall.

Marina thought how tall and handsome he looked, with his thick dark hair and a full dark beard threaded with silver. Wearing his naval uniform – so many shining brass buttons and so much gold braid – he was less her dear father and more the upright Commander Patrick Denham of His Majesty's Royal Navy. Marina came and slipped her small hand into his. He squeezed her fingers. He didn't say anything more, but turned back to the sea chart. The house was full of maps and charts collected over the years by the seafaring Denhams. This one was different: her father had drawn it himself, many years before, 'as an amusement', and it depicted the path to an imaginary realm marked on the map as the 'Drowned Sea'. An expert draughtsman, he was also a talented artist. Marina followed his gaze and studied the strange sea creatures whose domed heads he had drawn breaking through the curls of inky waves.

'Narwhals . . .' her father said. 'Such strange creatures. Hunters prize those horns. They are said to have magic properties.'

How Marina wished for a piece of narwhal horn! Then she could have enchanted her father to stay.

'A narwhal's tusk can be ten feet long,' he continued. She traced the domed heads and the vast unicorn spikes which were raised in salute with her finger. 'They are like sabres,' her father told her. 'Narwhals fight to the death. Their ability to start a meaningless fight is rather like the king and the archduke, don't you think?'

'But there won't be a war!' Marina looked at her father's face for signs that he was joking.

'Really? And how would you know?'

Her heart was beating faster. Why was he saying these things? 'Ivy told me.'

Her father shook his head. 'And how would Ivy, spending her day with the coal scuttles and tins of polish, know more than our prime minister?'

'Ivy reads all the newspapers!'

He looked surprised. 'And when would she do that?'

'When she's making up the fires.' Marina felt herself getting flustered. 'She knows everything the prime minister has said. And the king. And the Mordavian archduke! There's no navy that can match ours. We have dreadnoughts!' Marina thought about those British warships like floating castles on an iron-grey sea. Impenetrable.

'The archduke's navy is not a patch on ours, it's true,' her father admitted.

'I told you!'

'At least, not yet. But the Mordavians are building a new navy. I've no reason to think they won't succeed.'

'So what? We still have better boats and the bravest men and . . . You've said yourself that your men would rather drown with their ship than give an inch to a

13

Mordavian boat!'

'Perhaps that is no longer enough,' her father said gravely.

'What do you mean? What boat could be better than the *Neptune*?'

'It's not only boats with gun turrets and steel hulls that give you command of the sea, Marina. There are other ways of conquering that realm . . .'

'Mordavian submarines!' Marina exclaimed. 'They are too small to attack a British warship! If the Mordavians could fit guns to their submarines that could blow a hole in the hull of a British warship, those submarines would be too heavy to surface. The weight of the guns would make them sink to the bottom of the sea!'

Her father smiled down at her. 'You and Ivy really are very well informed.' His eyes narrowed as he said, quietly, 'But if the Mordavians don't have submarines with guns that can sink a British warship, then why have four of our boats gone missing in the Sea of Murmansk in the last month alone?'

Marina was so surprised that she couldn't think what to say.

'Ivy hasn't mentioned it to you? But I thought she was so well informed!'

'But what could be powerful enough to sink a British

warship?' Marina was confused. Ivy had definitely said that the Mordavian guns were useless against the steel hulls of the new dreadnought class of warships.

'Ah, but there are things on heaven and earth – and especially in the deep sea – that have not been dreamt of in Ivy Smith's philosophy! And what our housekeeper reads about in the newspapers is not necessarily a true account of what has happened in the northern seas.'

'But your ship won't disappear?' Marina suddenly felt anxious for her father. She tugged at his sleeve.

Her father laughed. 'Disappear?' He shook his head. 'Oh, no, Marina. I am an excellent navigator. I will always know exactly where I am! And I am taking the *Neptune* to Cadiz, which, the last time I checked, is nowhere near the Sea of Murmansk and those disappearing boats.'

He looked at his watch; one of the new sort favoured by naval officers and attached to his wrist by two leather straps. 'Almost time.' He looked at her as if he were only now really seeing her; his eyes crinkled at the corners and deep grooves ran from his nose to the corners of his mouth. 'How I hate goodbyes.'

'Let me come with you.'

'Ah, but young ladies and boats don't mix. It makes the men unhappy.'

'That's stupid!'

'The sea is a dangerous place, Marina.'

Her father had always said this whenever she had begged him to take her to the seaside. Edward joked that her father thought she was made of soap and would dissolve into lather if she got wet.

'I'll work hard. I'll hang the hammocks,' she insisted. 'You said that Perkins will only sleep in a hammock. And I can help Brown. The one who still gets seasick in a storm. I'd climb the rigging if there was still rigging to be climbed! I've been practising in the large plane tree in the garden all summer. I'm as quick as a monkey.'

'We have men to do those jobs, Marina.'

'But I'm as good as any man.'

'And so you are. But those men have families who need the money they're paid for working on my ship. Mrs Brown has another baby on the way.'

'Can I come to Portsmouth and see you off?'

Her father's eyes clouded, then. 'No, Marina. It's easier if you stay here . . .'

He turned away. He really was going.

Marina grabbed his sleeve. 'But I want to see your ship,' she blurted out. 'I want to see the *Neptune*.' She rattled off the specifics of the boat – Edward's endless droning on sometimes came in useful. She gave an accurate account of the *Neptune*'s tonnage, its speed, its hull shape. She even pulled out the length of rope she kept in her tunic pocket. Anything to keep him from leaving for a few more minutes. 'You said that every good sailor can tie a hundred knots. Well, I can! Look!' But her hands got in a muddle under her father's intent gaze. She felt her cheeks get hotter until her father took the length of tangled rope out of her hands. He gently unknotted it and she watched closely as his hands threaded the rope through several loops.

'Practise this one: it's called the pearl fishers' knot,' he said, handing it back to her. 'You know that, at sea, the ropes are rarely dry when you need to tie or untie them. This knot works when the rope is swollen with water. It's hard because of the double loop. Especially if it's freezing and you are wearing fur-lined gloves.'

Marina thought of the box which had arrived yesterday morning. R. SOLOMON AND SONS, WHITECHAPEL had been stamped on the lid. FURRIER.

'This knot saved my life on a remote island one winter, and brought me something very special.' Her father frowned and whispered something that made no sense. 'A pearl from beneath the ice.'

Marina could see from his eyes that he was journeying alone amongst his thoughts. She didn't want him to

17

leave her a moment before he needed to.

'Was that when you lost your toe?' she asked him. She pulled on his sleeve to bring him back to her. She loved her father's stories, but he only rarely gave her glimpses of his seafaring life and, like being allowed just a tiny piece of chocolate, it only left her wanting more.

He looked at her, surprised, as if he were waking up to find himself in a strange room. 'The very place. Almost lost my nose, too.' He tweaked her nose between his finger and thumb. 'Happy times, eh? Anyway, you train yourself to do that fiendish knot. And by the time you can do it with your eyes closed, I'll be home again.'

Her father put on his cap in a smooth, practised movement: his transformation was complete. He was all Commander Denham; no part of her father remained.

'Do I have to go to that dreadful school? I don't want to learn to sew or how to dance. If I must go to school, let me go to Edward's. It's in a forest and they write poetry under the trees and make their own chairs from the wood they gather.'

Her father didn't turn around. His voice sounded smaller than usual. 'You have spent your childhood without a mother, Marina. No one to teach you how to be a wife or a mother. You can't even wear a dress. How else will you be fit for the world if you don't learn these things?'

With those words, Marina broke the surface of her unhappiness. She could breathe. She could speak. 'I don't want to wear a dress! I don't want be a lady drinking tea in the parlour! I want to be useful. I want to have a job. I want to read the newspapers and have opinions and . . . and . . . march for votes for women!'

Her father turned then, a smile flickering at the corner of his mouth. Marina could see he was stifling a laugh. 'Work? March for votes? For women? What *has* Ivy been reading in those newspapers?'

'But, Father! Ivy says women will get the vote by next year.'

'Giving votes to housekeepers and parlourmaids?' He shuddered. 'Whatever next?' He picked up his kitbag and a large wooden case. It rattled alarmingly.

Ivy appeared from the kitchen, her plain face blotched, her wiry hair escaping from her hairpins. She dabbed her eyes with the corner of her apron. 'Go safely, Commander,' she muttered. 'I'll pray for your safe passage across the Bay of Biscay.' And she shivered. 'Oooh, I couldn't even make it past the pier at Margate when I went with my sister last Whitsuntide. How you manage on those raging waves . . .' The Commander frowned. Ivy stopped.

And as the clock in the hall delivered its six chimes, Commander Denham, ever punctual, bent to kiss Marina on the top of her head. Marina closed her eyes, willing him to still be there when she opened them.

The front door slammed. The clock ticked on.

3

Ivy tutted. 'Well, he's gone.'

Marina opened her eyes.

'And who knows if he'll ever come back.' Ivy shook her head. 'It's a sorry day,' she said as she turned to go down the stairs. 'Are you ready for tomorrow?' she asked. 'Can you go and check your uniform list and put your clothes in the trunk? Mind you do it carefully. I've got all my jobs to do before shutting up the house. It will just be bread and butter for tea. The Commander had the last of the cutlets for lunch.'

'I'll keep out of your way,' Marina said, feeling more wretched than she had thought possible.

'There's a good girl.' Ivy looked relieved. 'And have a bath, will you? You look filthy.'

There were strict rules about drawing a bath in the Denham household which made the whole process an unpleasant affair. The water was not only to be cold, but there was to be very little of it. In fact, after his wife had left seven years before, Commander Denham had painted a thick red line on the inside of the deep bath: it was to be filled no higher. But today, angry with her father for leaving for Portsmouth, Marina turned on the taps – hot as well as cold – as far as they would go and watched with a thrilling sense of defiance as the water gushed out.

She put her foot up on the side of the bath and inspected it. There was a patch of scaly skin on her right foot. Had it got bigger since the morning when she had pulled on her socks? She couldn't be sure. She prodded it with her finger. It didn't look sore but the skin itched and burned, like bad chilblains. It had kept her awake last night.

She folded her clothes neatly and put them on the stool. The water thundered into the bath. It was half full already, the water blurring the line of red enamel paint. How she had hated sitting in what seemed like a thimbleful of water. Today she would bathe like an Egyptian queen with hot water up to her neck.

The minute she climbed over the side of the bath and her foot touched the water, it stopped itching. She sank down into the water, looking up at the large lead cisterns which had been installed by Commander Denham for his bride thirteen years before. Marina had very few memories of her mother, and the memories she did have had been dulled by time. She shut her eyes as her limbs floated around her. She called up a hazy vision of a pale face with large dark eyes. There was long dark hair, like trailing seaweed. Ropes of pearls that hung down over the stiff boned bodice of a green silk dress with lace ruffles, like white caps on waves. And two canes topped with mother-of-pearl leaning against her chair, which her mother used if she had to walk. But Marina couldn't remember her walking, only being carried by her father. When he lifted her up, Marina could see the many large metal clasps on her mother's heavy black boots. She had always been frightened of those boots and had had nightmares where they became fixed to her own feet and pinched and squeezed her until the tears came. However hard she tried, she couldn't take them off.

Marina lay back and let her legs float slowly upwards.

The water rushed into her ears – such a beautiful sound. She closed her eyes and let her face sink under the surface.

A bright image floated up in front of her.

Her mother's face looking down at her.

Marina wanted to reach out and touch that face.

But this was just a memory, from the time before the red line had been painted on the enamel. It was from before her mother had left. It was from the time when her mother – although an invalid – had lifted Marina over the edge of the bath and lowered her on to the surface of the water. Marina remembered that feeling of the water suddenly on her back and crying out in alarm, but her mother had held her fast. And so, reassured, Marina had relaxed and floated on the gallons of warm water, kicking her little legs and reaching out her hands to try and touch the ropes of pearls that hung down from her mother's neck. Her mother had smiled.

And now, the water deep and warm, other images crowded in – she couldn't be sure if they were real or invented. Because there was her mother's face above, but it was blurred, as if it were being seen through water. And surely she was not remembering the sensation of having a heavy weight on her chest as if a stone had been put there . . . Or that she was sinking. Marina shook her head and the water in the deep bath gurgled in her ears. But she could still remember, or imagine, her mother's small hand on her chest all those years ago, pushing Marina under the water. Marina remembered – it did feel like a memory – that she struggled. She couldn't breathe. She tried to cry out but the water filled her mouth and anyway her mother was still smiling and, although normally so frail and weak, her hand could have been made from tempered steel. Marina remembered that she couldn't break free. Her chest had ached with the desperate need to breathe . . . 'Mama . . .' But her cry was silenced by bathwater and her frightened tears could not be seen.

Her mother's hand was snatched away. A rush of water, a gasp of air. Marina had been pulled up, coughing and spluttering, from the water.

Her father!

'Annabel!' he had cried. 'What are you doing?'

From the safety of her father's arms, Marina saw how her mother's eyes had clouded and her beautiful face had become sullen. She said nothing. 'She's just a child, Annabel,' her father had whispered. 'You promised me you would never . . .'

Her mother's deep green eyes had flashed their defiance as she wound her pearls tightly round her

25

fingers. Still she spoke no word.

A sharp pain stabbed Marina's chest. She was still submerged! She sat up abruptly. The water rushed off her head and body, slopping over the sides of the bath. She drew in a huge gulp of air. How long had she been under the water? Seconds? Minutes? *Hours?* But that was ridiculous. No one could hold their breath for that long.

She hopped out of the bath and snatched at the bath sheet, wrapping it around herself. She reached down to release the large metal ball which acted as a plug. There were goosepimples on her skin, but she didn't feel cold.

4

The morning dawned with fearsome brightness. 'The day of my execution,' Marina said to the ceiling. Perhaps she could just refuse to get up? What could Ivy do then? But she knew Ivy was ordered to pack up the house today, before she went to her sister's in Kent.

And Edward was already knocking loudly on the front door. She hauled herself out of bed and dressed in the hated school uniform. First, the regulation calf-length brown serge skirt. Then the regulation blue cambric blouse. The four regulation winter vests and the dancing slippers were already in her trunk. None of these ghastly items had any decent-sized pockets. And as for the ridiculous boater which scratched her scalp . . . She pushed her sailcloth trousers and tunic into the blue sailor's kitbag she had demanded for her last birthday. Perhaps she could wear them on Sundays to go walking in the countryside. Perhaps she could walk as far as Edward's school. The thrilling seafaring tale her father had written for her, which told of a lonely mariner pursued by a kraken, was stuffed on top of these comfortable, practical clothes. She pulled the drawstring tight and heaved the bag on to her shoulder.

She dutifully allowed Ivy to hug her and tell her how smart she looked, and how her 'dear mother would be so proud'. And then, moments later, still chewing on her crust of bread, she was outside on the pavement with her trunk. She and Edward were to be driven to the train station by Mr Mount's chauffeur. They were to take the same train; Edward's school in the forest was the stop before Marina's sorry lady-making destination.

'You look a total idiot,' Edward said, good-naturedly. He tipped her boater off her head on to the paving stones. Marina wanted to jump on it. She eyed Edward's loose cotton shirt and corduroy trousers with envy.

'Everything I wear itches,' she muttered, bending over to scratch that patch of skin on her foot.

Mr Mount appeared. Edward's father was a short, stout man with thinning blond hair and a boyish face. He wore a crumpled linen suit, no waistcoat, and, instead of the more commonplace tie and starched collar worn by men of his age and class, he had knotted a flowered silk scarf around his neck. This declared he did not work in a bank or a government department but that he was an artist – a good one, apparently; certainly his paintings sold for enough to pay for his large house, cook, maid and nanny, as well as the new motor carriage and chauffeur.

Marina wiped her hand on her skirt before shaking his hand. 'Good morning, sir,' she mumbled.

'Now, now, none of that "sir" nonsense!' He beamed. 'Why not call me Jonty?'

'Oh, I couldn't possibly,' Marina's eyes widened.

Edward laughed at her shocked expression. 'Because of what your father would say?'

Marina nodded.

'Don't expect he'll hear you,' Mr Mount said. 'Go on! Try it!' He winked at her.

'Good morning . . .' Marina felt her cheeks get hot. 'Er . . . Jonty.'

'There! You've done it!' He called to the chauffeur. 'Stryde! Get these trunks loaded!'

The man touched his cap and heaved the luggage into the open boot.

Mr Mount checked his watch as they climbed into the back of the motor carriage. 'Plenty of time, plenty of time,' he muttered to himself.

'Stryde likes to let the engine run before we get going,' Edward explained. 'He says it clears out the pipes. We can be sitting here for ten minutes if he thinks there's too much dust.'

'No need to panic just yet.' Mr Mount looked anxious. 'Edward. Have you brought your sandwiches? And the cake your mother made at midnight when she was so restless? She wouldn't give any to me! Said you'd be hungry on the train. I was hungry last night! Oh, I remember when I was your age I was hungry all the time. Didn't matter how much I ate. Pudding. Potatoes. Seconds of everything. Thirds if I could. Cleaned my plate. And still I wanted more! And I was thin as a pin! Can you believe it?' He patted his stomach and smiled. 'Ah. Youth.'

Marina thought that she would happily give up eating seconds of Ivy's lumpy mashed potato to be a grown-up and able to do as she wanted, but felt that she probably shouldn't say anything.

The engine noise increased and the motor car

moved forward. This was the life! How modern. How *new*. If only she were going to Portsmouth instead of to the hated Havering Ladies' College. She looked out of the window at the stucco houses, as large as battleships. What would she give to be on the *Neptune* with her father.

The moment the motor carriage drew up at Waterloo, Mr Mount's attention was taken up by bellowing for a porter to get the luggage into the station. 'That's right, my good man!' he cried. 'We're in a dashed hurry, so no messing about.'

The concourse was a baffling churn of people. 'Wait here while I get the tickets,' Mr Mount boomed. 'Edward, see the porter doesn't wander off. Those trunks need to stay right here for now. And you'd better look at the board and find the platform for the Winchester train. It won't be long! It's due to leave in seven minutes. Seven minutes!' he tutted as he hurried away.

A group of soldiers walked past, laughing. 'You? Brave?' one of them jeered at the youngest, a sleepy-eyed young man. 'You'd run away from yer own shadow!'

The young man's cheeks flamed. 'I'll stand and fight,' he muttered to himself. 'You see if I don't!'

'Gawd 'elp us.' An old man with grey whiskers took off his hat and scratched his head. 'If that's all that's saving us from the Mordavians!'

'Platform seven.' Edward scanned the departures board. 'Leaves in five minutes. Here's father with the tickets.'

Mr Mount hurried them on to the platform and explained to the porter where he was to take the trunks. He gave the man a sixpence, patted Edward on the shoulder, but then, overcome with emotion, pulled him in for a hug.

Edward pushed him away. 'Stop it!'

'I can't help it! I'll miss you, Edward. I'm going back to a house full of *women*! Who will protect me from all that endless female *chatter*? I'll need a box of wax earplugs!'

Marina thought this monstrously unfair and was about to speak up – tell Mr Mount that she had never heard him say anything remotely interesting himself – but then remembered that Ivy had told her to thank him for taking her to the station.

'I've got to go!' Edward stepped back.

'All right, all right. You go. The train is there. The trunks are being loaded. Nothing can go wrong now!' Mr Mount dabbed his eyes with a large handkerchief.

'Embarrassing or what?' Edward muttered, walking quickly away. 'I do wish he wouldn't do that. Did you see those soldiers laughing?'

'Train to Winchester! Platform seven.' A guard in a trim suit waved a small red flag. Steam billowed from beneath the engine, accompanied by the shush of the pistons.

'Quick, let's get on here.' Edward tugged at Marina's sleeve as he jumped up on to the steps of the nearest carriage. 'We can find our seats when we're on.'

'Train to Portsmouth! Platform six!' A shrill whistle blew.

Marina's head snapped round to see the train on the next platform. The guard had started to wave his flag. Another guard was walking up the platform shutting the doors. A group of sailors suddenly started running towards an open one.

'You go!' Marina shook her arm from Edward's hand. 'I . . . I . . .' She started to run across the platform.

'Marina! You fathead! That's the wrong train!'

'For you,' Marina shouted back. 'But not for me!'

A guard had seen her and was waving his arm to get her to hurry up. He held the door open and pushed her up the steps, slamming the door behind her. Another whistle. The train shook, there was an enormous blast

33

of steam and the hiss of the pistons filled her ears. They were off!

She pulled the window of the door down and waved enthusiastically to Edward, who was still standing, as if paralysed, on the steps of the Winchester train.

She laughed at his expression as a guard bundled him inside the carriage and slammed the door. 'Have a good term, Edward,' she called. 'Don't worry about me! I'm going to see my father!'

She pulled her head in: the steam was too intense. She leant against the panelling to catch her breath. She realized something extraordinary. For the first time in weeks – no, much longer than that – she felt a strange fizzing in her blood. She wouldn't go to that wretched school just yet. How she hated having to do as grown-ups told her because they 'knew best', when it was clear that they didn't and were just saying so to force her to go away, or not bother them, or fit in with their dull and boring plans. No more of that! She could make decisions – and very good ones they were, too – for herself.

'So *this* is what it's like,' she said to herself, shrugging off the feeling of being told what to do like shrugging off a coat on a warm spring day, 'to feel . . . *free*.'

5

As the train rocked from side to side, Marina slid open the door to the corridor and walked past the compartments. Where should she sit? The train was full of sailors, heaving their kitbags on to the luggage racks above the seats. They must be going to Portsmouth to join their ships. The men's noisy good nature was infectious. They were behaving more as if they were going on a village outing than to board battleships.

Marina finally found an empty compartment after walking through six packed carriages. She slid open the door. It smelled of stale tobacco and plush seats heated by the sun. She wrinkled her nose as she pulled open the top of the window and sat down next to it. She took off her ridiculous boater and threw it on a seat near the door. The breeze ruffled her hair and she set herself to watching London slip away. She had done something very foolish, but she didn't care! In a matter of hours, she would be with her father again. The thought of what might occur once she had seen him nibbled at the edges of her mind. But she pushed it away. She put her feet up on the seat opposite and leant her chin on her hand in a thoroughly grown-up pose. There was no need to worry, Marina told herself. She was thirteen next birthday! She pulled the hated ribbons out of her plaits and threw them out of the window. She shook her hair loose. She was quite the young woman now, and as such, what she thought and said was different to the babbling of a mere child. When her father saw her, he would have to listen to her. And she would have the whole train journey to perfect her plea to stay with him on board his ship. Yes. That was her plan. She would promise to work so hard that he would not be cruel enough to send her away. Her father had said that a mere girl could never join the navy. A mere girl would not be welcome on a ship. But she was no ordinary girl, after all. She was a Denham, the last in a long line of sailors and seafarers. Why couldn't she go to sea?

The train steamed defiantly through soft green fields. This was only the second time Marina had left London in her life, and the other time she could hardly remember. Where was Edward? Her stomach gurgled and she realized that she would have enjoyed sharing his sandwiches; Ivy had not packed any for her.

'Tickets!'

She heard the guard's cry with alarm. She'd had no time to buy one! She only had her ticket to Winchester. She hastily took her feet off the seat opposite – what had she been thinking? – and sat up straight.

The compartment door slid open and a small, ratty-looking man peered in at her. 'Ticket, young lady.' He smiled, showing two large yellow teeth that would have been very useful for chewing through ropes or sacks on board a ship.

'I'm afraid I've only got this one.' Marina fished out her ticket from the waistband of her skirt and handed it to him. 'I didn't have time to buy a new one. I was going to school, you see. But then I saw this train and thought I could go and see my father. He's in Portsmouth. About to leave. For Cadiz.'

The ticket collector had taken her ticket, given it a

37

cursory glance and held it out for her to take. 'No good for this train,' he said. His eyes now gleamed with malice. 'So you'll have to hop it.'

Marina, panicked, looked out of the window. The train was tearing through fields filled with hay ricks turned into golden pyramids by the sun.

'You'll throw me into a field?'

'Or you can buy a new ticket,' he sneered.

'I can?' A surge of relief. 'Oh, thank you.' Marina had brought all the money she had in the world. How rich she had felt when she had emptied her money box on her bed and counted the coins several times just to be sure of the grand total. 'Eleven shillings and a ha'penny,' she'd sighed, happily.

She reached for her purse. How fortunate to be rich. 'That's fifteen shillings – as you're sitting in first class,' the ticket collector smiled a tight, mean smile. Marina swallowed.

'Is there a problem, inspector?' A young woman in a neat blue-and-white striped suit with a white ruffled blouse had appeared in the corridor behind the guard. She wore a small straw hat perched on top of a pile of exuberant auburn hair

He turned and looked at her, his mouth open. 'There *is* a problem. And it's sitting right there. This urchin has got on my train without a ticket!'

The woman's mouth twitched in amusement. 'The "problem" seems very well dressed for an urchin, don't you think, inspector? And on the way to a smart new school, looking at the uniform.'

'That's all part of the charade,' the man sneered. 'But in all my years on the trains, I've never seen an urchin as brazen as this!'

'I didn't mean to get on without a ticket,' Marina said quickly. 'I just wanted to see my father. Oh, please don't put me off the train. His boat leaves Portsmouth at three o'clock ...'

The woman looked concerned. 'Don't worry, inspector, I'll get the child's ticket.' She reached into the large leather portmanteau she was carrying and pulled out her purse. 'How much is a half to Portsmouth?'

'Tickets are meant to be purchased before boarding the train,' the man muttered. But he got out a notebook and wrote out the ticket.

'I'm sure the child won't make the same mistake again.' She handed over a pound note. 'Keep the change. For your trouble.'

The man quickly pocketed the money – a tip so extravagant that he didn't want the woman to reconsider – and handed over the ticket. Giving Marina a strange look, he stepped aside to let the young woman take her seat.

She sat down opposite Marina, placing the large leather portmanteau carefully on the seat next to her. She smoothed out her skirt and smiled brightly. She looked like an illustration in Ivy's *Society News*.

'Thank you so much,' Marina said, blushing. 'I will pay you back, I promise. As soon as I see my father, I'll ask him for the money.'

'Perhaps next time you decide to board a train without a ticket and very little money, you should sit in the third-class carriage.' The woman clipped her consonants when she spoke. Where was she from? Marina wondered. The woman wagged her finger. She was wearing very clean white crocheted gloves. Her skirt was so daringly short that it showed an inch of calf above the top of her neatly laced red boots. She undid her jacket, revealing a bunch of silk pansies tucked into the waistband of her skirt. 'And what are you doing on this train? Are you going to school? That uniform looks very like the one I used to wear at my dreadful school. Brrr . . .' She shivered. 'It didn't matter how many layers I wore, I was always cold. The matron insisted on keeping the dormitory windows open all day, all night, even in the dead of winter.' While she was talking, she produced a tin of boiled sweets and offered Marina one. She took two for herself.

'I *was* going to school,' Marina said, pushing the sweet into her cheek while she talked. 'But when I saw the Portsmouth train, I thought I could go and see my father.' She swapped the sweet over to the other cheek. 'Before he leaves for Cadiz.'

'Cadiz?' The woman frowned. 'Is he sailing on the *Neptune*?' She pulled off one of her gloves with her small, even teeth.

'How do you know that?'

She put out her hand. 'Miss Gaby Smith, secretary to the First Sea Lord. So I know all about the British naval ships. And their sailors. What's his name?'

'Commander Patrick Denham.'

'But he doesn't have a child . . .' Miss Smith shook her head emphatically. 'Unless the details in his file are wrong.' She pulled a face as if she were making a very hard calculation in her head. And then, without any warning, she laughed, dimpling her cheek. 'And yet here you are.'

'Here I am.'

'He's a good man, Denham. Signals expert. Worked in Room 40.' She glanced at the compartment door and leant forward, dropping her voice to a whisper. 'Room

40 is where they put the really clever chaps. The ones who can make up codes that bamboozle the enemy.'

'My father is very good at crosswords,' Marina offered.

'And he speaks a lot of languages. That's always helpful. Do you take after him? Are you good at languages and puzzles?'

'Oh, no,' Marina said, hastily. But Miss Smith looked even more interested.

'You'd be surprised at the information I find in those dusty old files,' she went on. 'No one else thinks to read them. Your father is very musical. I found that out by reading his file. A lot of people who are good at mathematics and codes are musical. I suppose because music is just another code, after all. Perhaps you are musical?' She raised an eyebrow.

Marina's father had banned her from singing, or indeed any sort of music. He said he found her voice 'upsetting'. But this she could not admit to the woman sitting opposite.

'Oh, I am *very* musical,' Marina said. The thing to do when telling a lie was to *really* believe what you were saying. She could tell Ivy all sorts of nonsense about how she had brushed her hair or eaten her crusts as long as she just believed that she hadn't thrown her hairbrush behind the chest of drawers or pushed her crusts into the kitchen range. This entrancing woman was not Ivy, of course, so she'd have to watch her step.

'You are? What instrument?'

Best to keep things simple. 'I sing.' The woman's eyes were now nicely widened in admiration. Marina racked her brain for the sort of detail Ivy had given her after coming back from listening to Nelly French at the music hall. 'My father says I can trill like . . . a nightingale in May. I take after my mother.'

Miss Smith's eyes flashed with a blaze of interest. 'Your mother had a good voice?'

'Oh, yes. Her voice was quite *enchanting*.' Marina tried to sound offhand. As if all the Denham women could sing like nightingales. But the young woman was observing her closely, as if she was trying to work out if Marina was speaking the truth.

She looked out at the fields, tugging her hair around her face to hide her blushes. She didn't want to answer any more questions about her mother or her mother's voice. Because of course her mother could not sing a note. How could she? Her mother could not talk. Her mother had been a mute. It made Marina feel ashamed when she thought of it, even though her father had explained that being unable to speak did not mean that her mother was stupid or feeble-minded. But Marina felt that her mother's silence meant something – something that was not good. Why else would Ivy refer to the long-absent Mrs Denham as 'that poor, dumb creature'? Why whisper that 'the poor woman couldn't tell us how unhappy she was'. Why add, in such sad tones, 'but she had very *speaking* eyes. Like a sick animal.'

'Perhaps you might sing for me?' Miss Smith's voice blew away Marina's thoughts like a dandelion clock.

'Oh, no.' Marina shook her head, flustered. Did the woman suspect that she was lying? 'I can't sing just *like that*.' She thought of how Mr Mount's chauffeur had grumbled about the dust getting into 'the pipes' and had let the motor carriage engine run for a few minutes before they set off for the station. 'The steam from the engine is not good for my vocal pipes.' She coughed.

'One day, perhaps.' The woman smiled and Marina smiled back, feeling on safe ground again, but she went on, 'I could find somewhere where the air is cool and not so dry and scratchy and your voice will enchant everyone who listens to it.'

'Yes. I'd like that.' Marina nodded a little too enthusiastically. 'I'd like that very much.'

Miss Smith held out her hand and they shook on the promise.

6

The train clicked and clacked. They heard an enthusiastic roar from a carriage full of sailors. And then the men broke into a sea shanty.

'Your father spends a lot of time at sea.' The woman was pouring tea from a flask she had pulled from her portmanteau. She handed the cup to Marina. 'Which must make things rather lonely for you, I think?'

'Our house makes him feel sad. It reminds him of how life was before my mother left us.'

'Your mother left you? Your mother – with the enchanting voice?' The woman looked concerned. 'Do you mean she ... she ... passed over?'

Marina shrugged. *Passed over. Gone before.* These strange ways of saying that you would never see some-one again.

Miss Smith unpinned her straw hat and placed it carefully on the seat next to her. 'How very sad for you,' she said, quietly. 'But you look like her.' Miss Smith narrowed her eyes and looked very closely at Marina's face.

'I've been told that I do.'

Miss Smith was observing Marina as if she were a painting in an exhibition. 'Because you don't look like your father. Your eyes are such a pretty shape. And your hair is so black it has a lustre, like mother-of-pearl. Your skin looks very delicate too.'

'I'm not sure whether I look English or not.' Marina shifted in her seat. The skin on her foot was itching and she fought the impulse to pull down her sock and scratch it. 'I suppose I just look like me.'

The woman smiled and nodded as if she agreed. 'Which is quite the best way to look. Although I am shocked at how badly brought up you are. Quite the rudest young woman I have ever met.'

Marina scanned Miss Smith's face for signs that she was joking, but the woman looked quite stern.

'I-I don't know what you mean?' Had she offended

the woman somehow?

'Here you are talking to me, and not bothering to introduce yourself!' Miss Smith's face twitched in amusement.

'I am Miss Marina Annabel Denham.' Marina gushed. 'How do you do, Miss Smith.' Marina shook the woman's hand.

'Very well, as you were kind enough to ask. Although a little hot. I had to rush from the office.'

Office. Marina sighed in admiration. 'Oh, I want a paid occupation when I grow up, but my father wants me to get married and arrange flowers and write out menus for the cook and see that the coal merchant gets paid, and a whole lot of other boring rot. I ask you!' Marina tried out the snort of derision she had been practising on Edward all summer.

'Urgh.' Miss Smith shuddered. 'In other words, he wants you to be that ghastly thing: a *young lady*. Which is about as appealing to a bright girl as being a plate of chopped liver. But not as useful! And no doubt your father thinks this is what will be best for you?' Miss Smith raised one eyebrow. Marina nodded. Miss Smith flared her nostrils. Marina copied her but it made her sneeze.

'I wonder, have you told him how you feel? Perhaps

if he understood how you wish to make your own life rather than have one handed to you, he might let you choose how you spend this one miraculous existence you have been given?'

'It's hard to explain to him,' Marina said, quietly. Her father did have a remarkable ability to silence her. Not by shouting; not even by not listening. He would simply nod slowly and then change the subject. Even Edward had not believed her when she said she was determined to choose her own path in the world. 'I'm sure you'll do whatever you want,' he'd said. 'But have you really thought about how difficult it will be?'

'What do you mean?' she'd asked.

'Well . . . Who will look after your babies?'

'Why is that my job?'

'Just saying . . . Babies tend to be quite fond of their mothers. Even though Maudie is five and should be happy to be with our nanny, she won't leave Mother's side for a second. And mother can't stand the crying so she lets her stay.'

'Maybe babies should be trained to be fond of their fathers!'

Edward had looked sceptical. 'Good luck with that, Marina.'

Marina looked at the young woman in front of her,

who had so far resisted the lure of motherhood and the dreaded fate of being a 'young lady', and was working in the real world, not seated on a velvet-upholstered chair in a parlour waiting for her husband to come home and tell her what had happened in the world beyond the room's four walls.

'But what do you do? For your job?' Marina felt as if Miss Smith might have some secret which she must discover if she were ever to choose her own life.

Miss Smith put her head on one side. 'Let's see. I write reports. I file memoranda. I check the communiqués coming into the Admiralty. I am very good at what I do. I have to be. There are many men there who do not believe a woman can spell, let alone compose reports! My work is not very interesting, perhaps, but it's the life I chose. It's mine and no one else's. And it does have its charms. Today, for instance, I am not sitting in the office trying to fit a complicated naval problem into a cablegram of fifty words. Instead, I am travelling incognito to Portsmouth on important Admiralty business.' She glanced at her leather portmanteau. 'I have to give last-minute orders to one of our men, who is sailing deep into Mordavian waters. As you can imagine, such orders are too sensitive, in the current climate, to send by cable.' She leant forward and whispered, 'There are spies *everywhere*. I can't risk these instructions being intercepted.' She put her finger to her mouth, signalling that she had just told Marina something of great importance. 'Please don't give me away!' She winked and smiled her dimply smile. 'But as you are the daughter of Commander Denham, who is known to keep so much to himself, I feel I can trust you.'

'Are there really spies everywhere?' Marina asked. She felt thrilled to be talking to this fascinating woman.

'I think there may well be a spy on every British boat.'

Marina gasped.

'If I were the First Sea Lord,' Miss Smith went on, 'which of course I can never be, as I am but a frail woman –' she made her voice tremble comically, which made Marina laugh – 'I would make sure that there was a sailor on every boat who answered directly to me. I would make that sailor give me daily reports about the behaviour of every other member of the crew.' She looked out of the window. 'Do you know what makes a good spy?'

'No.' Marina could have kicked herself. If only she could have thought of a better answer.

'Noticing things. Small things. Even things that don't seem to matter. I sometimes make myself look

50

around as if I were a spy. I force myself to see things that ordinary, silly people wouldn't. I have trained my eyes to notice things – like the way that you keep scratching your foot, or how you didn't want to sing. And then I wonder what those two things might mean.'

Marina felt rather important to have been the subject of such intense scrutiny, and uncomfortable at the same time.

'And the puzzling fact that there is no mention of you in your father's file. You should train yourself, too. Write things down in a notebook every day. Remember, it's the little things you see that others might miss. If you were a spy, what would you notice about me, for example?'

'Oh . . . Well . . .'

'The First Sea Lord would not read a communiqué that started like that!'

'You're wearing a very short skirt . . .' Marina started.

'Go on,' Miss Smith encouraged her.

'I think it makes you look very *new*.'

Miss Smith clapped her hands and laughed. 'Exactly! That's the sort of detail that is very important! Now, are you hungry?' She opened her portmanteau and brought out a greaseproof-paper packet. 'I made biscuits. You could write that in your report: "The subject made biscuits. It means that she does not like to go hungry when she is working. It suggests that if she were to skip a meal, her judgement might be affected." That's the sort of thing you would need to notice and include in your report.'

She unwrapped the package and handed it to Marina. Inside were small iced stars. Marina took one and bit into it.

'What do you think?' Miss Smith asked.

'Oh, they're delicious!' Marina said. 'Should I put that detail in my report?'

'Of course! Now take another! Biscuits should never be eaten singly.' She pulled a serious face, but then dissolved into a fit of giggles. Marina laughed, too.

After finishing her biscuit, Miss Smith took a tiny silver-backed looking glass out of her bag and, scandalously, applied a deep red stain to her lips. She could see Marina staring and smiled. 'Very good for feeling brave,' she explained. 'If I have a difficult task to complete, I always put on my war paint!' She put her 'war paint' away. 'Have you been to the seaside before?'

'Oh, no!' Marina said. 'Although I've begged my father to take me.' What she didn't add was that this refusal to take Marina to the seaside came only after her mother had left. And no one had told her why. She frowned, the merest scrap of a memory flapping at the corner of her mind. Her mother sitting on a rug on the sand, her green silk skirt spread out around her. Marina shook her head slightly to try and see the scrap more clearly, but she couldn't focus on it.

'I think all children should go to the seaside,' Miss Smith said, thoughtfully. 'The sea air is so bracing. It's very good for their lungs.' She frowned. 'So your father has never taken you anywhere? Abroad, perhaps?'

Another scrap of memory. Her mother carrying her, quickly, towards the waves – her legs must not have been hurting her that day. Where was her father?

Marina shook her head again to dislodge the picture. It couldn't be anything more than a fancy brought on by the excitement of the journey. Her mother couldn't walk without two canes, let alone carry her child across an expanse of sand . . . and into the sea . . .

'My mother wasn't well. And then my father was at sea . . .'

'What do you remember about your mother?'

Marina gulped and shook her head. 'Hardly anything. I was very young when . . .'

'But your father must have told you about her?' Miss Smith raised an eyebrow.

Marina felt as if she should say that her father talked about her mother often. But he was away so much, and when he was at home, his work took all his time. What could she remember about her mother that would make any sense? She felt her silence disappointed Miss Smith, but the woman smiled as if she understood.

'It is the same with my father. He died when I was small. It upset my mother to talk about him. So she didn't. Parents don't always know what's best. They try to keep us from suffering but don't see the harm they are causing.'

That was a shocking opinion, Marina thought.

They finished the biscuits and ate an apple apiece.

Miss Smith now pulled some papers out of her portmanteau and started to read them. Marina felt that she, too, should have an occupation. Clearly, clever women – the sort who wore short skirts and worked at the Admiralty and looked at every person as if they were a potential spy – were never idle. She pulled her length of rope out of her kitbag and attempted the fiendishly difficult knot her father had shown her the day before. But the knot got tangled and wouldn't come right. She got flustered.

'What are you doing?' Miss Smith looked up from her papers.

'Just tying knots,' Marina said in an offhand manner. 'I practise all the time. My father says a good sailor can tie a hundred different sorts.'

Miss Smith nodded. 'But that one is proving quite difficult,' she commented.

'It's the best knot for icy conditions,' Marina explained. Why wouldn't the loops lie flat? 'My father showed me how to do it before he left.'

'Well, he won't be needing that knot in Cadiz!' Miss Smith smiled.

'How hot is it in Cadiz?'

'Oh . . . boiling, I should think.'

'Even at night?'

'Of course.'

'So no need for fur-lined gloves, then.'

'I would think only a mad Englishman would wear fur-lined gloves in Cadiz. Why do you ask?'

Marina shrugged her shoulders and looked out of the window.

The rest of the journey passed quickly. Miss Smith was an amusing companion with lots of stories to tell about her work at the Admiralty, her landlady, and her childhood in Northumbria, 'Where I acquired my strange accent,' she joked. When the train steamed into the station at Portsmouth, they gathered their belongings, feeling quite the best of friends.

Miss Smith took Marina with her in her cab to the docks. And there they parted.

'I must deliver my orders,' she said. 'But promise me you will meet me here at a quarter to five and we will travel back to London together. I will see you home.' She frowned. 'Although it's probably best not to tell anyone – especially your father – that we have met. He was very against women being allowed into the Admiralty, and may make my task harder.'

Marina felt suddenly anxious that she might be returning to London later that day. Her plan to go to sea seemed foolish now she was here. 'Yes . . . Of course . . . I'll meet you,' she mumbled.

'Are you sure you're going to be all right, dear heart?' Miss Smith asked, her forehead creased with concern.

'Oh, yes,' Marina replied in what she hoped was a confident tone. 'I'm going to see my father. He'll be so pleased to see me!'

'Just don't let him carry you off to sea! It would be unbearable for me to have made such a charming and pretty young friend only for her to run away.'

7

Marina had imagined herself standing at the harbour and gazing out at the infinite, ever-moving sea – feet apart, her kitbag on her shoulder, having grand thoughts about how women must be allowed to work for the Admiralty. Women as clever and accomplished as Miss Smith (and as clever and accomplished as she passionately wished to be) must not be confined to parlours and nurseries. She would not be told what to do. She would shout her defiance to the waves!

The reality was rather different.

There was no wide horizon to accept her cry.

Portsmouth harbour was preparing for war. It was taken up with steel hulls and gun turrets: enormous dreadnoughts docked in black and oily water. They had no interest in the voice of a twelve-year-old girl. There was no fresh, salty tang, only the sour taste of coal and oil and steam. Marina wrinkled her nose in distaste. Why did the world have to be so different from her dreams?

Marina found the harbour master's office eventually. Miss Smith's cab had dropped her at the wrong end of the docks and she'd had to trudge past three enormous battleships and ask two porters before finding it. Her kitbag, although it only had her trousers, tunic and book, felt as if it were stuffed with live octopuses, and the patch of itchy skin on her foot meant that she had to keep bending down to scratch it. Her thick school socks had chafed the skin until it bled. It was already two o'clock.

Inside the office, Marina waited in a queue until it was her turn at the desk.

'Could you tell me where the HMS *Neptune* is berthed?' Marina asked a harassed-looking clerk.

'*Neptune*? She's berth nine. Next one down on the left. If you've got a letter for a sailor, you'd better hurry. The tug boat has been called to tow her out.'

Marina got held up behind a tide of carts carrying

fruit and vegetables, and then she had to wait while a crane unloaded crates. Everywhere, men crying out, 'Watch it! Step aside! Coming through!' More than once Marina was pushed to the side by an impatient cart driver or hauler.

But she found the HMS *Neptune*. And she was beautiful. Marina looked up at her steep sides – enormous panels of steel riveted together and painted pale grey – and then tipped her head back to take in the gun turrets. No wonder this ship was the pride of the British navy. And her father was the Commander!

She started to climb up the gangplank.

'Oi! Young lady! What are you doing?' A young sailor stood on deck. 'No civilians allowed on this boat!'

'It's all right – I'm here to see my father!' Marina called out.

'Who's that?'

'The Commander of the ship,' Marina said with what she hoped was enough confidence to convince the sailor.

He frowned. 'Well, you'd better hurry up, then.' He whistled her up. 'We're almost due to leave. The minute that last crate of fruit is loaded, we're off. The tug boat's here and we're ready to go!'

'Oh, thank you, thank you.' Marina felt a rush of gratitude.

'Does the Commander know you're coming? I wasn't told there'd be visitors.'

Something in his tone sounded like a warning.

'Of course!' Marina smiled at him and accepted his hand as he helped her off the gangplank and on to the deck. 'Oh, this ship is such a beauty,' she said, looking around admiringly.

'Indeed,' he agreed. He hailed another young sailor and told him to 'escort the young lady to the bridge'.

'Not sure they'll thank me for that,' the sailor said, frowning.

'They'll chuck you overboard if you don't! It's the Commander's daughter, you lemon!'

The sailor quickly saluted Marina, which delighted her. If only she could get her father to agree to let her stay . . .

She was taken up metal stairs, sailors turning to stare at her. Now that she was only moments away from seeing her father, she realized that her thumping heart might not be excitement. It could, possibly, be fear.

'What's she doing 'ere?' a sailor growled as she walked past.

'Bringing bad luck,' his companion muttered.

'Permission to bring a visitor on to the bridge, sir!'

Marina took a deep breath to try and get her hammering heart under control. She looked into her father's domain: dials and instruments, a hydrophone for speaking to the engine room, and the barrels of two enormous guns shadowing the prow in front and framing the view of the sea. A man in a navy-blue jacket with gold at his shoulders and sleeves surveyed the horizon, where sparkling sea met a watercolour blue sky.

'Papa!' she cried.

The man turned, a look of surprise on his face. 'Who . . . Who the deuce are you?' This Commander was the same height as her father and had the same short, dark hair threaded with silver. But he was not her father.

Marina faltered. 'But . . . you're not Commander Denham!'

'I am not, young lady! I am Commander Barham. And I would like to know how the devil you got on to my boat!'

'She said she's your daughter, sir!' The young sailor had snapped to attention as the Commander looked at him, eyes blazing.

'I'm Marina Denham. And my father, Patrick Denham, is the Commander of the HMS *Neptune*.'

The man's eyes flickered. 'There's no one of that name on this ship, my dear,' he said, not unkindly. 'I think you must have made a mistake.'

'But my father *is* Commander of the HMS *Neptune*.'

'I am the Commander of the *Neptune*, my dear,' the man said. 'Now I don't know how this mistake was made, but I'm sure they can tell you which ship your father is on in the harbour master's office. That's where they keep the lists of the men and the boats.'

He turned away. 'Have the Chief Engineer start the engines, Marshall.' His voice was sharp: a man used to being obeyed.

'Yes, sir!' The Second Officer unhooked an ear trumpet and mouthpiece. 'Orders from the bridge. Start the engines!'

Marina was bustled down the metal stairs and marched down the gangplank. No sooner was her foot on the dock than the sailor turned and ran back up to the ship. The gangplank was pulled up. The HMS *Neptune*, the Orion-class dreadnought of His Majesty's Imperial Navy, was leaving Portsmouth.

Alone on the quay, Marina dropped down on her haunches and watched the dark, oily water churn and slap against the dock. The powerful engines of the HMS *Neptune* were creating a wake that would rival the work of any sea god. She watched as that vast floating citadel edged away from the port: it didn't seem possible that there was enough water in the ocean to hold up so many tonnes of guns and steel.

Only now did she fully realize the hopelessness of her situation. She was in Portsmouth rather than being met from a train somewhere in Hampshire. More worryingly, she had no idea where her father was or how she could contact him. The harbour master's office had no record of her father or any boat he was commanding. Perhaps he had left already? Feeling unmoored, she walked slowly to the edge of the quay. She would have to wait for Miss Smith, as she had promised.

The briny tang of the sea called up another sea, another time. A puzzling collection of images and sensations jostled their way into Marina's mind. The imagined day on the beach with her mother reappeared, as if floating on the dark water in front of her. She was held tight, against the ropes of her mother's pearls. They hurt her ear. She tried to pull away, but her mother held her even tighter. The water! The sea! It was splashing up into her face, cold and salty. 'Mama...' Marina had cried out then, shocked by the chill droplets on her skin. And then she roared as an icy wave caught her foot. But still her mother plunged forward, holding Marina so tightly she couldn't wriggle free, however hard she tried.

The pictures in Marina's head were chased away by a yelp. She looked up to see a large wooden crate of dogs on a cart next to her. Who they belonged to she couldn't tell, but they looked hot and cross in the afternoon sunshine: their coats were so thick Marina thought she could bury her hand in them. One had his tongue lolling out and was panting as if he were a pair of bellows. He had one bright blue eye and one a soft treacle brown.

'Oh, hello.' She edged nervously towards him. His eyes made him look curious and comical, not scary at all.

Edward had always said that he wanted to have a 'whole pack of hellhounds', but Marina, although she liked dogs, was in truth a little scared of them: they always seemed to snap at her, even the butcher's sleepy Labrador, who lay in the doorway of the shop on the High Street, eyeing the bags of the customers who stepped over him, hoping for a piece of faggot or some bacon rind.

'It's because you fidget,' Edward had explained one afternoon as he sat on his branch of the copper beech.

'You've got to stay calm and let them sniff you.'

'Urgh, that's horrible.' Marina had wrinkled her nose in disgust.

'How else are they going to get to know you? I suppose you could give them a visiting card with your name on, Marina, but they can't flipping read!'

These fluffy creatures were unlike any dogs she had ever seen; they looked at her with intelligent curiosity, their ears two triangles atop flat, furry faces. The dog with the odd-coloured eyes put his head on one side, as if he were waiting for her to explain why on earth he and his friends were being kept waiting on the quay of Portsmouth docks.

'What are you doing here?' Marina held her hand towards the bars of the cage. 'Are you in a muddle, too?'

The dog pushed his snout through the wooden slats and sniffed her. His nose was cool and damp. It tickled. She laughed, in spite of herself. She pushed her hand through the cage and stroked his ear. He pushed his head up into her hand. 'Oh, so you like that, do you?' she whispered.

'Perkins? Perkins?' shouted a sailor with a shiny bald head from the deck of a rather decrepit fishing boat. 'Get over 'ere. Get those dogs on board! We're leaving in ten, mate!'

'I'm here, Brown!' A tall, lanky man with his hair tied in a ponytail waved his arm dismissively. 'Quit your caterwauling!'

Perkins. Brown. Marina knew those names! Every letter her father had written to her from every tour he had been on had described the funny things they said. These men were due to be sailing with her father – on the HMS *Neptune* to Cadiz!

On the side of the rusting hulk, just visible, though most of the paint had been worn away by salt, water and wind, a name: *Sea Witch*.

The man called Perkins approached the crate. The dogs barked and whined and became restless.

''Scuse me, miss.' He smiled at her. 'I've got to get these villains away, now. They're going on a long voyage. Come on, boys! I'll make sailors of you by the time I'm through.'

'Where are they going?' Marina asked.

'Now that would be telling, little lady.' The man tapped the side of his nose with his finger. 'And however you look at me with those big, sad green eyes of yours, I can't tell you! I'm sworn to secrecy.'

Marina tried a little sniff, and blinked, hoping for a tear, just to see if it might prompt the man to tell her something more.

Her beseeching look must have made the man think again. 'Let's just say –' he winked at her – 'that these little furry lads with their thick, warm coats won't feel the cold! Oh, yes, they'll feel right at home!'

He whistled a shanty with great enthusiasm as he pushed the cart towards the boat. But he huffed and bent forward with the effort of getting it up the steep gangplank. 'What they been feeding you?' He laughed, good-naturedly. 'Rocks?'

'Watch it, Perkins!' Brown cried as he watched the dogs being pushed up the gangplank. 'You drop them dogs in the water and Commander Denham will have *you* pulling the sledge!'

So this was her father's ship!

Perhaps it was the agitation of the day. Perhaps it was the anxiety over her train ticket and her lack of funds to pay back Miss Smith. Perhaps she was merely hungry: a boiled sweet, two tiny biscuits and an apple is not food enough for a brain to work sensibly. It couldn't be the fact that her father had lied to her. There must be a reasonable explanation as to why her father was not commanding the *Neptune* and sailing to Cadiz. But try as she might, Marina could not think of it. She felt strangely lightheaded as she watched the dogs being shoved on to the boat. As she stood there, the sounds of the dock fell away and she felt the ground tilt. A sound of water rushing towards her, through her, made her shake her head. When the sound had ceased, she looked around. Everything looked the same, but felt different. Anything, in that moment, seemed possible.

'The thing is,' she said to herself, picking up her kitbag, 'Miss Smith offered to take me back to London, but I have no money to pay her back for the fare. Ivy has packed up the house and gone to her sister's in Kent. I've no idea how to get to that dreadful Ladies' College, and not enough money to get there even if I had.' She took a deep breath. 'I can't go back ... So I'll just have to go on ...'

She heaved her kitbag on to her shoulder and walked purposefully towards the gangplank of the *Sea Witch*.

8

The hull was pockmarked with rust but, once on deck, Marina could see that the *Sea Witch*, though old, was spick and span. She crept along the newly varnished deck, keeping an eye out for sailors. She saw Perkins, his back to her, fixing the hook of a winch to the top of the dog crate. The animals were going to be lowered into the hold. They stood up and barked with excitement. Marina tripped over a large coil of thick rope and then quickly ducked down behind a small lifeboat, capable of holding no more than twelve men.

Crouched here, she realized how stupid she was.

What was she doing, cowering on a fishing boat about to sail to who knew where? If found, no one would believe that she'd climbed on board to say goodbye to her father. They'd think she was a stowaway, and her father had always been clear that those miserable wretches who neither worked nor paid for their passage were harshly treated. As if angry at her folly, the *Sea Witch*'s engines growled. The deck beneath her feet shuddered. She peered over the side and saw the urgent swirl of black water. A sailor on the quay pulled a mooring rope off a bollard and threw it up on to the deck of the boat with practised ease. She heard the garrulous clanking of the anchor being raised as the man sprinted along the gangplank. She should stand up now. She should run towards him and tell him that she had made a dreadful mistake and that he must let her off.

She hesitated: the man looked angry, his forehead creased in a surly frown. And he was quick. In seconds, he'd leapt aboard and was drawing up the gangplank – and in doing so, removing her means of escape, the only way she could get back on to dry land.

'Gangplank stowed!' It was done. She was trapped, with no way of leaving the boat that didn't risk drowning.

The boat heaved forward, as if impatient to be out of the confines of its narrow berth.

'The dogs are secure?' a man's voice called out over the noise of the engines.

'Aye, sir!'

'Then let's get to sea. We've a long journey to the ice, and the Commander's in a hurry to get there!'

'Aye!' men's voices answered enthusiastically.

'To the north!' the man cried.

The male chorus roared in ragged unison: 'To the north!'

Marina clutched the guard rail as the boat swayed beneath her. She had to make herself known. There would be a dreadful row, but she had to be put back on the quay. What had possessed her to climb on to this boat? It was going north, whereas her father had been clear that he was sailing to Cadiz. Was it possible that there were two Commander Denhams? Two Browns and Perkins? She tilted herself over the side. The water churned angrily as if it were boiling. Could she jump into that and survive? Panic drenched her. The sides of the dock seemed very high; there was no clear way that she could climb out of that water back on to the dock, even if she made it that far – her father, who thought that a deep bath was dangerous, had never taught her how to swim. This water certainly did not look as if it

71

would hold her up and let her thrash her way to the quay; it looked as if it would swallow her and drag her to her death, just as her father had always warned her.

'You'll get yourself into trouble one day,' Edward was fond of telling her. 'You're so *impulsive*.' But she remembered how he always smiled as he said it. 'I'd really like to be around when you do get into trouble. Because, blimey, will it be fun to watch.'

Well, this wasn't fun. Her hands gripped the rail even tighter. If she could only risk raising one leg off the juddering deck, she could climb over and jump. Anything was better than staying where she was and being discovered. She put one foot up, her heart pounding. And then, looking back at the quay, she saw something which made her hesitate. Standing near the bollard where the *Sea Witch* had been tied up was a young woman in a blue-and-white striped suit, the skirt thrillingly short. The woman's auburn hair was tucked under a little straw hat and a leather portmanteau had been dropped at her feet. But what was so surprising about Miss Smith was that she had a pair of binoculars round her neck. And she was looking at the departing *Sea Witch* – looking right, it seemed, at Marina.

Her father had always given voice to many superstitions: it came with being a sailor. But one of his most fiercely held was that it was bad luck to speak to anyone with red hair before a sea voyage. Marina swallowed. Had she brought bad luck to the *Sea Witch* by talking to the fascinating Miss Smith? But, she reasoned, she hadn't known that she would be going on a sea voyage at the time when she had left Miss Smith on the docks. And could someone who had called her 'dear heart' really bring bad luck on a voyage?

The woman raised the binoculars. Marina ducked down. She couldn't bear the thought that Miss Smith would see her, a silly schoolgirl, a wretched stowaway, cowering on the deck of a decrepit old fishing boat instead of being welcomed triumphantly on to a towering dreadnought by her loving father. The little boat heaved and shuddered as it caught a current. In those few moments, the *Sea Witch* had moved clear of her berth and the other ships moored at the dock. She was already in a channel of water and was turning, turning on a sixpence, towards the open sea.

A sharp breeze caught Marina's hair, caught her boater and blew it off her head and on to the black water. Marina peeped through the railings and saw it bob up and down on the threads of ragged grey lace that topped the waves. Seagulls swooped, hoping it would make a meal, and wheeled up, screeching their anger at being tricked. The dogs in the hold howled and barked as they tried to make sense of the unpredictable motion of the ship.

The awful, jiggling motion of the ship. Could it not just be still for one moment? Marina gulped in the sea air, hoping it would get rid of the sour taste in her mouth.

And then, without warning, she stood up and was very sick over the side of the boat.

The sea was choppy, the breeze off the water was brisk. Marina clutched her knees to her chest in the hope that it might stop the retching. Men's voices called to each other as they prepared the boat for the open sea.

'Secure the winch!'

'Get those nets stowed! And be quick about it!'

'Seal up the hold!'

Marina could still see the coast – the blessed, unmoving coast – even as the sea currents tugged at the boat's hull. The *Sea Witch* plunged up and down like a demented donkey. How many knots would a small boat like this make? Nine? Ten? But it would depend, too, on the depth of the waves the boat was labouring over. The northern waters, she knew, had waves like mountain ranges, but mountains that moved, swelled and toppled on top of any boat brave, or foolhardy, enough to sail to the Far North.

She groaned. She mustn't think about those large and violent seas. She tilted her head up: they were already in the Channel. The *Sea Witch* seemed to hold herself for a moment, as if deciding whether to go forward or not. And then she dipped into the wave, almost shivering with enjoyment. There was no enjoyment for Marina. This daughter of generations of sailors and seafarers was battling raging seasickness.

The air grew colder. The afternoon sun ground the waves to crushed glass. Marina rubbed her arms. 'There's no such thing as bad weather,' her father often said. 'Only bad clothes.' Her thin school blouse was very bad, then, as it gave her no protection from the wind. Swallowing another attempt by her stomach to force her to lean over the side, she pulled her sailcloth tunic out of her kitbag and pulled it on. The heavy cotton kept out the worst of the wind. She took a lungful of air and found that it calmed her stomach. The motion of the ship, however, was still a problem. The moment she tried to stand up, she knew she had to immediately crouch down again. She felt that if she could only be beneath the water, all would be well (a ridiculous thought). But this bobbing about on the swell was unbearable.

'What 'ave we 'ere?'

Before she could attempt to escape, her ear was almost twisted off her head and she was dragged, howling, from her hiding place. A large red face was thrust towards her, two eyes, round and brown as currants, narrowed in suspicion. The man was short, with thick arms and a barrel chest, his head bald. It was Brown, and his voice was even more stern and humourless now than it was when the boat was being loaded at Portsmouth.

'Let me go!' Marina gasped. She twisted and turned her body, but Brown had her in a powerful grip and if she tried to pull away, it only hurt her ear more.

'No point squawking,' he said, calmly. 'Even if you get free of me, you're not going anywhere. Unless you can swim!'

'Let. Go. Of. Me,' Marina cried, desperation making her chest tighten and her voice squeak.

Brown frowned and gave her request some thought. 'Right. I will. But you're to come with me, and quietly, to the bridge. The Commander'll want to see you. And then he'll decide what to do with you.'

The boat pitched and she lurched to one side.

'Trouble finding yer sea legs? Well, that's going to be nothing compared to the blast the Commander'll give you!'

'The blast he'll give *you*!' Marina had to speak quickly before the urge to be sick came over her again. 'You wait. He'll have you barnacled!' It was the rudest thing she could think of. But Brown just laughed at her bluster.

'Not the Commander's style to string a man beneath the hull of his boat, whatever he's done.'

'Don't you know who I am?'

'I don't care if you're the ruddy Queen of Sheba. You're going to see the Commander.'

He pushed Marina towards some metal stairs that led up to the bridge. The sudden fear: Brown was right – her father would be angry with her for missing her train, for not going to school, for losing her trunk and all the new, expensive things inside it. She had spoken out of desperation and misplaced bravado. She panicked. 'Maybe I could just wait a moment?'

'Not feeling so brave now?' Brown jabbed her in the back. 'Keep moving, miss.'

At the top of the stairs, an open door to the bridge. Could she make a run for it? But to where? Anticipating that she might do something foolish, Brown grabbed her by the elbow: there was to be no escape.

'Permission to come on the bridge!'

Marina hopped from foot to foot, willing herself not

to be sick on the spot.

A man in a rough blue fisherman's duffel coat stared out to sea. Without turning round, he took his pipe from his mouth. 'What is it, Brown?'

'Stowaway, Commander.'

Brown pushed Marina in front of him and on to the bridge. There was a high metal step which Marina tripped over; she only managed to stop herself from falling by grabbing the sleeve of a boy – two, maybe three years older than herself.

The boy snatched his sleeve away as if he'd been stung. She murmured an apology. And then, trying very hard to stand up straight even though the boat bobbed and rolled, she looked up into her father's face.

9

Her father said nothing. And this was worse than if he had shouted at her. The silence was so unbearable, the sour taste coming up from her stomach was so awful, that Marina thought she would be sick again. She swayed. The boy moved away from her. She reached out and steadied herself on a shelf of rolled-up sea charts. A sandy-haired man stared out to sea as if nothing was happening.

'I found 'er behind the lifeboat, sir,' Brown explained. 'And she couldn't make no account of why she was there. Although she expected you to be pleased about it, sir.'

Commander Denham did not look pleased. He did not welcome Marina on board. 'Jones,' he snapped at the boy, who was staring at Marina as if she had a contagious disease. 'Contact Room 40 at the Admiralty. Inform them I'll need a man dispatched to take care of a stowaway.'

'Room 40?' Marina blurted out. Why did her father want to contact Room 40? Miss Smith had said that this was where all the clever men in naval intelligence invented codes to bamboozle the enemy, or cracked enemy codes to find out what the enemy was planning. Marina imagined them hunched over their machines, furiously replacing words with numbers, or else cracking messages as easily as dropping eggs on the pavement. What would such men do to her? Marina was just a girl, not an enemy code! Why did her father need to speak to these men? 'Don't tell them anything about me!'

'What would *you* know about Room 40?' Her father narrowed his eyes with suspicion.

What could Marina say? She had promised Miss Smith not to tell anyone they had met and so could hardly tell her father about their conversation.

'Well?'

She crossed her fingers, knowing that she was lying and feeling bad about it. 'N-nothing,' she muttered.

Only once the boy had left the bridge did her father pull Marina towards him by the sleeve of her tunic. 'What is the meaning of this, Marina?'

'You know her, Commander?' Brown whistled in surprise.

'That's enough, Brown,' Commander Denham said, curtly. 'You'll speak when you're spoken to.'

'Aye, sir.' He looked down at his feet.

'Marina? I want an explanation for why you are not at school and are instead on my boat.'

Marina stared at the toggle on her father's duffel coat. She must not allow herself to see the horizon moving up and down, up and down. 'I . . . I . . . I was on the way to school. Mr Mount took me and Edward to the station. I was just about to get on the Winchester train. My trunk had been put on. But then the train to Portsmouth was on the next platform. I just wanted to see you . . . One last time.' She swallowed. Perhaps if she closed her eyes, she wouldn't feel so sick. 'I owe money to a very kind woman who paid for my ticket . . .' She opened her eyes again. Surely she could say that much without breaking her promise to Miss Smith? 'I was meant to see you on the *Neptune* and then meet her afterwards, but when I was put off the *Neptune* there was such a long time to wait before I could meet the

81

woman again.' Marina sniffed. 'Everything felt so hope-less. But then I met some dogs and I heard the names of the sailors – it was Brown and Perkins, do you see? And the day sort of tilted and rocked. And then I just ran up the gangplank. I didn't intend to be a stowaway. I really did just want to see you one last time before you left. But everything happened so quickly . . .' She blinked back tears. 'I've only eaten two biscuits and an apple all day. Apart from the crust that Ivy gave me. And that was stale. And now I've been sick. Oh, it was over the side of the boat, so I haven't made a mess.'

'Finchin?' her father said, not taking his eyes off her.

The pleasant-looking sandy-haired man now turned to the Commander. 'Yes, sir.' His clipped tones marked him out as a naval officer, despite the rough fisherman's sweater he wore. He spoke as calmly as if he were waiting to find out the time of a cricket match.

'We'll put my daughter off the boat at Kirkport.'

'Kirkport, sir? In Scotland?'

'We can't risk a larger port. They'll ask all sorts of questions.'

Finchin cleared his throat. 'Permission to speak, sir.'

'I know what you're going to say, Finchin. That a stop at Kirkport will hold us up. But what can we do? I can hardly take my twelve-year-old daughter on this mission.'

'With respect, sir, we are cutting it fine to get to Svengejar as it is. From there it will take another three days to get to the Sea of Murmansk—'

'You think I don't know where we're going?' Commander Denham interrupted.

'We need to get to Pechorin Island,' Finchin said, calmly. 'And without wasting time stopping at any unnecessary port . . .' He cleared his throat. 'We can't dilly-dally if we're to . . .' He coughed. 'Before . . .'

'But I thought you were going to Cadiz,' Marina blurted out.

'Where I go and what I do is none of your business,' her father snapped. 'I have a mission to complete. You – with your nonsense of playing truant from school and getting on wrong trains – have jeopardized it. And we're scarcely an hour out of Portsmouth!'

'Father. Please don't put me off the boat. Please let me stay. *Please.*'

'Stay? On the *Sea Witch*? It's out of the question. This boat is no place for a . . . a . . . *girl*.'

Marina gripped the shelf more tightly. 'I'm afraid . . . I'm awfully sorry . . . But I might just be . . .' She clapped her hand tightly to her mouth.

'Get her off my bridge, Brown. And quick! When she's been sick, you can put her in the hold until Kirkport.'

'Aye, sir. Shall I find her a hammock? Some spare galoshes?'

'Do what you like with her. Just keep her out of my sight.'

Out on deck, Marina sank down on her haunches and took gulps of the chill sea air.

'That was quite some stunt you pulled there, young lady.' Brown looked impressed. 'Although I don't know as how it has worked out very well for you. In fact, looking at the colour of you, I'd say it's worked out pretty bad.'

She put her head down on her knees. Brown didn't hurry her. 'Aye, we're not all born to be sailors,' he observed.

'But I'm a Denham,' Marina whispered on her sour tasting breath. '*All* Denhams are sailors.'

'Don't matter who you are or what your name is. The sea takes to some and not to others.'

She sniffed. 'Can't the sea stop . . . *moving*? Just for one moment?'

'The sea stop moving?' Brown laughed. 'Not while I live and breathe. Best get you lying down. That's the only way.'

'Could you just wait for a moment?' Feeling as she

did, Marina couldn't imagine getting up and walking down the steep stairs with all this rising and falling.

The voices of Finchin and her father drifted out on to the sea air from inside the bridge. They spoke of wind speeds and knots and nautical miles. It was all gobbledygook: the strange impenetrable language of the sea. If only she could speak this language as fluently – if only she, too, could make the sea her element.

Finchin's voice floated towards her. 'Shame Miss Marina isn't a boy, sir. We could've made her one of us.'

He spoke without any malice, as if he were simply stating a fact.

10

Brown pulled up a small trapdoor cut into the sealed cover of the hold. He knelt down and peered into the dark. Seeing the light and smelling the fresh air, the dogs started barking fit to burst.

'Oi!' Brown shouted at them good-naturedly. 'Enough with the chatter!'

Marina followed him down wooden steps, wrinkling her nose at the pungent smell of fish. They stood, swaying with the movement of the boat. It was a huge space, like being in a church.

'This is where they stored the fish when the *Sea*

Witch was a fishing vessel. Now it's full of our stores and some of the Commander's equipment.' Brown indicated a wall of wooden crates. 'And dogs.'

In the dank, close air, Marina retched again and sank on to the floor. Brown quickly strung up a hammock, all his movements quick and efficient.

'In you get,' he instructed her. 'Best place for you right now if you can't stand.'

She forced herself to get up again and staggered towards the hammock, but it swayed too much for her climb in.

'Steady as she goes,' Brown said, holding the hammock still while she awkwardly got in. She groaned and he threw a heavy blanket over her. The dogs whined and barked but she couldn't take any notice of them. Brown put a bucket near her head. 'In case you need it.'

What a dreadful end to her adventure. Her foolishness, more like.

'How long till I'm put off the boat?'

'We'll reach Kirkport in the morning.'

Left alone in her hammock, Marina thought she would drown, thought the boat would drown, thought the sea itself would drown. How else to account for the violence of the pitching and rolling that tormented her? It wasn't even that she could anticipate the strange movement of the boat: it would go up, causing her feet to tip into her body, but then it would roll to the side. Her hammock would swing so wildly she had to clutch both sides to stop herself from being flung out. *I'm being flipped like a pancake*, she thought.

The light faded, the hold grew dark. The dogs snuffled and settled down to sleep.

She didn't care.

The moon rose. A slice of silver shone through the porthole and cut her in two.

She didn't care.

All her life she had believed that she could take to the seas, like all those generations of Denhams before her. But now she realized she was one of those hated beings, spoken of with contempt by all sailors: a landlubber.

'If I could just get off this boat,' she told herself, 'and be *still*, I will never dream of going to sea again. I will live always in the middle of a green field surrounded by mountains.'

She was aware of Brown coming in from time to time. He asked how she was doing and she croaked the same reply. 'Awful . . . just awful . . .'

'Give it time, miss,' he'd said, good-naturedly.

'How long?' she'd whispered.

'Can't say's I know.'

He got her to sip some water, told her it would help. He cradled her head as he lifted a tin mug to her lips. The water didn't help. She sank back into her hammock, nauseous and exhausted.

A whole wretched night dragged by. But it would soon be over. When Brown came in at daybreak, she felt only relief. Soon this infernal motion would cease. Soon she would not feel sick. What a relief it would be to get off this boat.

'What time do we stop at Kirkport?' she asked.

'We've gone past it a couple of hours ago.'

'But I'm meant to get off there!' She sat up.

'We're not stopping nowhere this side of the North Sea . . . Seems like you're going to be with us for a while longer. But not because the Commander's changed his mind about you. Some Scottish fishing boat's gone missing in the Sea of Murmansk. The Commander's in an awful hurry to get up to there. To the north. Can't say as how I know how we can make much of a difference – we're only a crew of eight – but that's the Commander for you. He has a way of finding his way to where the trouble is . . . Think you can stand? Think you can get some seafaring clothes on you? I've brought you some galoshes and oilskins and a nice warm sweater. The wind is fresh. Must be up to ten knots or so. And the swell is high.'

'I know,' Marina closed her eyes. 'I can feel it.'

Brown opened the dogs' cage and let them out. They snuffled around the hold, exploring their domain. One of them – the curious dog with the different-coloured eyes – came up to the hammock and sniffed Marina's hand.

'He's a character, that one,' Brown remarked, changing the straw the dogs had slept on.

The dog made a funny yowling noise that sounded as if he were trying to speak; in fact Marina had the impression that he thought he *was* speaking. And he was expecting her answer.

'Well, thank you,' she whispered, tugging his ear affectionately. 'I feel as rough as sandpaper. That's what Ivy says when she's done a day of laundry. I do just wish the boat would stop moving for a moment.'

The dog gave this some thought and replied in his own way.

'They're not seasick at all,' Marina said to Brown.

'They're not. They're good little sailors, those dogs. Put up with anything. Now, you rascals, enough with the chat. Time to get back in that cage. Breakfast will be in an hour, miss. Reckon it would be good for you to try and eat something. Might settle that stomach of yours.'

Slowly Marina swung her legs over the side and, as long as she didn't look at the horizon swinging around through the porthole, she felt she might be able to stand. The dogs, seeing this, stood up too, as if they might all be about to go somewhere together. A few started yowling in that strange way, as if they had to tell her something extremely important.

'I can't understand a word you're saying,' she told them as she reached for the clothes that Brown had left out for her. 'But I'll go and find out all the news.'

She folded her blanket neatly. Sailors were always very neat: they didn't have the luxury of space at sea. She stripped off the hated school uniform, kicking it into the shadows between the crates of stores and equipment. She had no way of washing in the hold (what a relief). She ran her tongue over her teeth. They were slightly furry, but she didn't care.

'You don't need to clean your teeth, do you?' she said to the dogs. 'So why should I?' She pulled on the thick fisherman's sweater and rolled up the sleeves. The socks came up over her knees. Next came the stiff oilskin trousers, which were so large they looked like a clown's costume. The galoshes were too big for her too so she put her boots back on. She flattened her hair with her hands: her ribbons and hairbrush were packed in her trunk and therefore somewhere in Hampshire, rather than on the North Sea, where they were needed. Well, she couldn't be bothered about such things now. 'It's just vanity,' she told herself. A tiny flutter of excitement in the pit of her stomach. She was wearing seafaring clothes. She had not been put off the boat. She was to stay on the *Sea Witch*. Who knew what adventures she might have, so long as she refused to look at the horizon through the porthole. Or think of her father's fury the day before.

'I'll have to spend as much time as possible on deck,' she told herself. 'The fresh air will blow away the seasickness.'

She pushed open the trapdoor, blinked at the light, sniffed the air. She climbed out, her oilskins creaking. Once on deck, she took a moment to adjust to the swaying of the boat. The air nipped her cheeks and made her flattened hair fly around. Spume rose over the narrow prow. She staggered forward a few paces. The wind jostled her. The engines hummed, the waves jumped, the deck rolled. The coast had fallen away. She had the sudden impression that everyone had left her while she was in the hold, and that she was now quite alone on a small, fragile boat travelling across an immense and unknown sea. In her kitbag was the book her father had written for her last birthday. It was called *The Lonely Mariner* and told the sad tale of the captain of a two-masted brigantine. This poor wretch crossed the seas alone, always trying to get back to port but prevented by tragedy. The way her father had written the story, with the captain battling against storms, sea monsters and loneliness, made the sea seem a frightening place, awash with peril and sadness.

'I am no lonely mariner,' Marina told herself. 'I am a Denham. The sea is in my blood.' The sea didn't think much of that, and she almost toppled over.

She stood with her feet wide apart and tried to feel the movement of the waves. The trick was not to fight them, but to move with them.

A man appeared from behind the metal stairs and leant over the side of the boat. He, too, was dressed in oilskins and wore a knitted cap. It wasn't Brown or Perkins. It was the surly man who had pulled up the gangplank.

'Good morning!' she cried out.

He looked up, as if annoyed at being disturbed, and

disappeared towards the stern.

Brown had told her to go to breakfast, but where was she to go? Marina made her way towards the bridge, leaning into the wind, gasping at the way it forced itself into her mouth, her lungs. She tried the first door, but it was locked. The second, too. The third she wasn't expecting to open so easily.

A fog of tobacco smoke, and the sound of low, male voices.

'Good morning!' Marina said again, as brightly as she could.

11

The men fell silent. Through the porthole the horizon moved rapidly up and down and Marina knew that she couldn't stand up for very long. Her father sat at the table furthest away from the door, with First Officer Finchin on his left. The other men – Brown, Perkins, and the boy, Jones – faced her. The surly man who had just ignored her on deck sat with his back to her. He didn't turn round. The room – the 'mess', as sailors called where they ate – was very small, and Marina banged her leg on the end of the bench as she went to take a seat next to her father. Just as she was about to sit down, the room still silent, her father shook his head.

'This is the officers' table,' he said.

Brown nudged Jones and they moved apart slightly, giving her just enough space to climb over the bench and sit down.

Finchin cleared his throat. 'As I was saying. It looks like we've got a wind direction of a hundred and sixty degrees.'

'Speed?' her father asked.

'Sixteen, gusting up to twenty-one.'

'Any chance of precipitation?'

'None, sir.'

'And the swell?'

'Minimal, sir. Visibility is six nautical miles.'

Marina might as well have not been in the room. Her father didn't ask if she felt any better; he didn't enquire how she had slept or explain why she had not been put off the boat at Kirkport. Now that she had sat down, he didn't acknowledge her presence at all.

The boy next to her – Jones – stared straight in front of him, as if he were afraid to look at her. That wouldn't do. If her father ignored her, there was nothing Marina could do about that. He was a busy man – he had a boat to command and a mission to complete. But this boy wasn't much older than she was. Marina turned slightly

96

towards him and put out her hand. 'How do you do?'

Perkins snorted. 'Go on, Jones,' he said, good-naturedly. 'Answer the young lady. I'm sure even you've seen one of those before!'

'That's enough, Perkins,' the Commander said, before returning to his conversation with Finchin.

'Aye, sir.' But Perkins's mouth still twitched with amusement.

The boy ignored Marina's outstretched hand. 'Morning,' he muttered, his face flushed with embarrassment.

'I'm Marina.'

'I know who you are,' he hissed through clenched teeth.

'But I don't know who you are.'

The boy looked horrified.

'He's called Jones. We don't use first names in the navy,' Brown said kindly, filling a tin mug with tea. He added three sugars and plenty of milk before handing it to Marina. Ivy would have been horrified. 'That's Perkins. The quiet one is Trenchard. We've got Cook and his Mate in the galley and the Chief Engineer and his Mate in the engine room. They don't eat with us. The Engineer won't leave his precious pistons and furnace.'

The cook, round-faced, round-bellied and beaming, brought in a bowl of fish stew, and the Cook's Mate, skinny with two long front teeth like a rat, carried in a basket of freshly baked bread and a tin of butter. This was placed on the officers' table. The cook returned with more stew and bread for the sailors. Marina was about to reach for the bread when her father rapped on his glass with his knife. The men cleared their throats and looked down. Marina copied them. Her father said a few short words of prayer. Clearly things were different at sea: her father was not what Ivy called 'a God-fearing man' at home. The men heaped food on to their plates. All this – for breakfast! Marina still felt queasy, but took the bread roll Perkins handed her. She asked Trenchard for the tin of butter, but he turned his head to look out of the porthole as if he hadn't heard her request.

'Take no notice,' Perkins said. 'He was on the night watch. He'll be right as rain once he's had some kip. Won't you, Trenchard?'

The man shrugged.

Marina thought about what Miss Smith had told her on the train: how there was a spy on every British boat. Well, if that were true, this man would be the spy. She observed him from underneath her lashes. If she were writing a report for the Admiralty, as Miss Smith had suggested she practise doing, perhaps even marking it for Miss Smith's special attention, what details would she include? *Shaved head, small scar on left cheek. Sullen.*

The crew of the *Sea Witch* ate quickly and efficiently and then left the table. There was clearly work to do on the boat which did not allow them to linger over their meals. Used plates and cutlery were placed in a pail at the entrance to the very small kitchen – Marina knew it was called a galley – and she waited behind Jones for her turn to put her plate and tin mug there.

'Denham?' her father called.

She dropped her cutlery into the bucket with a clatter and stepped back into the mess.

'Yes, Father?'

'You'll address me as "sir". I am your Commander, not your father, while you are on this boat.'

'Yes . . . sir.' That sounded odd.

He slid a piece of paper across the table. 'Here. Read this and sign it.' He uncapped his fountain pen and held it out.

Marina looked at the paper. Under her name was a list of rules that she must obey. 'I'm . . . I'm . . . to be a member of the crew?'

'I'm not taking passengers on this boat,' her father said. 'And even if I were, I think you said you've not enough money. How much did you have in your piggy bank before I left?' She saw Finchin turn away, the flicker of a smile on his face.

'Eleven shillings,' she muttered, embarrassed that her money woes were being discussed so openly. 'And thruppence. I had nearly twelve shillings, but I bought Edward a toffee apple and then we had buns and I paid for his ticket to the circus . . .'

'An iced bun is excellent fare,' Finchin commented, filling his pipe with tobacco. 'Quite my favourite food when I'm in port.'

'Think before you sign it,' the Commander went on, ignoring Finchin. 'These are terms of employment. I won't have things unclear on my boat. You'll be treated exactly like any other member of the crew, no better, no worse.' Next to the word 'Rank', Marina read, 'Boy, 2nd class'. Of course, there would be no rank of 'Girl' on a British naval ship. Next to the word 'Pay', she read, 'Per diem, 6 d'.

'I'll get money?' This seemed the most excellent thing of all. She would have a paid occupation! If only she could tell Miss Smith.

'You'll work for it,' her father said, gruffly. 'I won't have idleness on my boat.'

*

100

Marina practically swaggered out on to the deck. What a turnaround in her fortunes. Only twenty-four hours ago she had been a stowaway. And before that she had been about to be a wretched schoolgirl. But now she had a paid occupation. If only she could tell Miss Smith that she was now a sailor. A 'Boy, 2nd Class'! What would she say if she knew that her young friend was a crew member of the *Sea Witch*? No French verbs or embroidery on this boat. And who needed kohl-rimmed eyes and silk pantaloons, like those silly 'new women' in Ivy's *Society News*, if you could dress in a fisherman's sweater and oilskins and be ready for real work?

But what work should she do? On her terms of employment, her daily tasks had just said, 'as instructed by the crew'.

She saw Perkins hauling a large fishing net across the deck. It looked awfully heavy. 'Let me help!' she cried.

12

Iron-grey, solid waves. Spray as cold and sharp as razors. Perkins could not have heard her over the wind and the noise of the engine. He did not look up from his task.

She snatched at the net; the rope was thick and rough.

'Watch it, miss,' Perkins cried. 'That's too heavy for you.'

'I'm very strong,' she shouted into the wind. 'Ivy gets me to carry all the coal upstairs at home.'

But now she had the rope in her hands, she could feel the real weight of that mass of fishing net. She pulled and she pulled. It didn't move.

'You're pulling the wrong way,' he shouted at her. 'I'm taking it over there.' He sounded a bit cross.

'Sorry!' Marina shouted back. 'I've got it now.' She tugged again. She thought her back would break. Her arms were being pulled out of their sockets. 'Ow!' Perkins had tugged sharply on the rope when she wasn't expecting him to and it badly burnt her hands. She dropped the rope and blew on her palms to try and stop the stinging.

'I'm sorry, miss. You've got to let me get on with this,' he said, gruffly. 'The Commander wants these nets in the water by noon.'

She looked around. What else could she do?

'Go and find Brown. He'll give you a job,' Perkins said, dragging the net towards the winch, his movements easier now that he wasn't being impeded.

Brown was carrying two large canisters – like milk churns – across the deck.

'Let me take one,' Marina said, trying to take one of the handles.

'Aye, there's no need.'

'No, but I'd really like to help. I'm one of the crew, now.'

'That's as maybe. But I don't need your help, miss.'

She hadn't taken her hand away. Why didn't he just

give her one to carry? The boat pitched, she stumbled and the canister came with her. It fell to the ground and rolled away down the deck.

'Not sure as that's much help,' Brown grumbled as he ran after it.

She was too frightened to ask the surly Trenchard, so she leant against the winch practising her rope-tying in an effort to impress the sailors. She even did some sailory whistling. It must have worked because Brown soon found her a bucket and a brush. 'Why not clean the little lifeboat over there?' he said to her. 'It could do with a good scrub.'

At last. Something she could do that would show what a hard worker she was.

The bucket had a long rope attached to it. She gingerly let it down over the side of the hull and a wave filled it for her. She pulled it up; how could water be so heavy?

And then she got down to the task of scrubbing the small boat's hull. She looked over her shoulder a few times to check that Brown and Perkins were watching: she wasn't a slacker!

They seemed pleased with her efforts, nodded their approval, and got back to their tasks.

Cleaning the boat was hard work. Her elbows hurt.

Her shoulders were sore. She was soaked because the bucket kept tipping over. When she filled it from the sea, it was so heavy and awkward lifting it over the guard rail (and she didn't want to ask for help) that once or twice she lifted it all over herself. But she wasn't a quitter. She would show Brown and Perkins how useful she could be. Trenchard walked past. She redoubled her efforts but he looked unimpressed.

She felt pleased with her hard work but, even so, she was relieved when the bell rang and the men left their work to go into the mess for lunch.

'What did you do to the Boy?' Commander Denham stood up from his chair and looked at the poor bedraggled creature who stood, dripping sea water, on the floor of his warm, dry mess.

'The Boy wanted to be useful, sir,' Perkins said, looking sheepish. 'But the Boy ain't got the strength for the nets.'

'So I asked the Boy to clean the lifeboat,' Brown said. He was having trouble keeping a straight face. He looked first at Perkins and then at the floor.

'Couldn't you think of anything else for her to do?' Finchin was trying to frown, but he, too, struggled to stop an amused grin breaking through.

Marina squirmed. She was wetter inside her oilskins than outside. But that feeling of discomfort was not as bad as the men's suppressed merriment at her expense. Hadn't she done a good job cleaning that boat?

Brown pulled himself together. 'No, sir. But to be honest, we didn't think the Boy would take to the job with quite so much enthusiasm.'

Marina looked down at her hands, red with rope burn and the angry scratches from the bristles of the coarse metal brush. What a fool. Of course that boat didn't need cleaning. They'd just given her something to do to keep her out of their way.

Jones came in and sat down in his place. He gave Marina a startled look. She pulled her wet hair out of her face and tried to look as normal as possible, which was hard. Now that she was inside the warm fug of the mess, her sweater gave off a cloying smell of wet sheep.

'Is there anything the Boy can do?' the Commander asked, looking as if he knew full well there wasn't.

'Not anything *useful*,' Brown admitted, as if it pained him to tell the truth. 'I asked Cook if he'd have her. But he says there's no room in the galley and his knives are too sharp for someone with butterfingers.' He looked apologetically at Marina as if he only told the truth reluctantly.

The Commander sighed. 'After you've eaten, Denham, you can go and help Jones in the Signals Room.'

'Perhaps the code books need dusting,' Finchin explained, quite pleasantly.

'Sir!' Jones protested. 'I don't need any help, sir!'

'You'll have the help you're given, Jones. That's an order.'

Marina knocked on the door of the Signals Room. No answer. She knocked again. She shouted Jones's name. Still no answer. She opened the door, just a crack. Jones turned round, alarmed, as a gust of air rustled a pile of papers on his desk.

'Oh,' he said. 'It's you.' He pulled strange-looking earmuffs off his head. His black hair stood on end. 'Sorry,' he said, his cheeks turning pink. 'I didn't hear you. I'm listening.' He pointed at the earmuffs. 'I'm waiting for a message from Room 40.'

The room was scarcely bigger than a cupboard. There was no porthole. Light came from a single oil lamp, which swung from the low ceiling. Jones pulled out a stool for her. They had to sit so close together that their shoulders brushed, which didn't bother Marina – she and Edward often had to sit close together on their tree-climbing expeditions – but Jones obviously found it awkward, hunching his shoulder away from her. Now that Marina – there to be helpful, as ordered – was in the Signals Room, he didn't seem to know what to do with her.

'Why don't you tell me how the machine works?' said Marina, after a few moments of awkward silence. 'Perhaps then I can think of a way to be helpful.' In front of her was a large, handsome mahogany case set with dials and gauges and clock faces. Needles and spirit levels and clock hands moved and jumped and swung in erratic rhythms. There was also something like the barometer in the hall at home, which was meant to predict the weather but more accurately predicted whether Ivy would moan about her arthritis. Then there were switches and a row of tiny brass levers along the bottom. Oh, and this was the best: wires with pegs on the end that needed to be fixed to small metal keys. Even playing a church organ, with two keyboards and all those stops and pedals, couldn't be as complicated as working this machine. Lights flashed and Marina could hear an odd noise, like the insistent dripping of a tap. How could Jones, still a boy, have any clue what he was doing with all this machinery?

'It's a signals machine,' he muttered.

'Is it difficult to work?'

'It's what I'm trained for,' he mumbled. Jones had delicate hands, like a pianist. And he was very thin. He would have been just as useless on deck with Brown and Perkins as she was. 'I had to get a trade, see. I couldn't go down the mines, like my da . . . I couldn't breathe down there and they had to bring me up.'

'But what do all these dials and lights and wires do?'

'You don't know?' He glanced at her, frowning.

'No.'

'But your father built this machine.'

Marina remembered all the boxes and packages her father had received while on shore leave, and the hours he'd spent locked away in his study.

'I thought maybe he might have shown you . . . As he's a signals expert . . .'

'He doesn't talk to me about his work,' Marina said. This comment seemed to puzzle Jones. As though any other father would have enjoyed explaining the workings of a machine he was taking the trouble to make. But her father never thought that Marina might be interested in any aspect of his life. At least, that was how he behaved. 'My father doesn't talk very much at all,' she added, as if this might explain her father's reluctance to describe how he had made such an intricate machine.

She looked again at the switches and gauges, the little keys and the wires attached to them. 'It looks very complicated. What does it do?'

Jones looked a little more cheerful. 'What doesn't it do?'

'Well, I don't think it can make tea, can it?'

'I think it probably could.' Jones almost laughed. 'Only I haven't got to that page in the instruction manual.' He cleared his throat, remembering that he was the *Sea Witch*'s Signals Boy, doing serious work, and not someone who could be distracted by his Commander's only daughter. 'Your father is such a brilliant man, though, I think he could build a machine that could do just about anything.'

Marina liked the boy's voice. It had a sing-song quality, going up and down like the waves. She wondered where he was from. Not Hampstead, anyway.

A small round light flashed amber. 'Weather forecast,' Jones muttered. He pulled the earmuffs back on to his head and listened intently, writing something down in his notebook.

Apart from listening out for the Admiralty-issued weather forecasts, Jones explained that the machine could send and receive messages.

'Like telegrams?' Marina said.

'In what way?' he asked, suspiciously.

Well, there he had her. She had no clue how telegrams worked. Jones could have told her they were delivered by pixies and she'd be none the wiser. Well, perhaps the pixies could deliver a message now. She gave Jones a nudge in the ribs.

'Let's send a message to Miss Smith!'

13

'Miss Smith?' He looked completely unimpressed. 'Who's she?'

'You must know! She's the secretary to the First Sea Lord himself.' Marina was going to say that they had travelled down on the train to Portsmouth together and that they had become great friends and that she had called Marina 'dear heart', but she remembered her promise not to tell anyone of their meeting and stopped herself just in time. In any case, Jones was giving her a look that implied that he didn't believe a word she was saying. 'I've heard that it's Miss Smith who sends all of the communiqués. I've heard that she's very good at her job, even though there are plenty of men in the navy who don't think that women should do more than make their tea.'

'A woman? Working at the Admiralty?' Jones pulled a face. 'Who did you hear that from?'

'Maybe I could just send her a message?' Marina said, rather than answering. She reached forward and flicked one of the switches.

'Don't touch that!' Jones snatched her hand away. 'Sorry,' he apologized. 'It's just that the machine is very delicate. You have to be very careful. That's the switch that lets me listen out for other ships. So there are no collisions.'

'Collisions? But the sea is so huge! How can boats sail into each other?'

'And you the daughter of Commander Denham,' he said, shaking his head. 'Boats can't just sail about wherever they fancy. There's such a thing as a shipping lane.'

'What's that?'

'Like a path or a road. On the sea. And the ships have to use them.'

Marina laughed. 'How can you have a road of water?'

Jones looked offended. 'Think what you like. It's the truth.'

Just at that moment, the machine started chattering and a tongue of white paper emerged from a narrow opening. Jones tore the paper off and was about to stamp it.

'Could I do that?' Marina asked.

Jones shrugged. 'Fine. Then put it in that metal basket up there.'

She felt very pleased with herself as she took the heavy brass stamp, pressed it into a red inkpad and then pressed it down on the paper. It left the date. But what had been printed on the paper made no sense. Did Jones not realize?

'What do those squiggles mean?'

'Your father is sending a coded message and that graph shows the strength of the signal on that channel there.' He tapped a green light. 'Your father likes to check every four hours that the message being sent out into the water is strong.'

'A message? Into the water? But who could hear a message in the water?'

Jones's cheeks turned pink. 'Sound waves can travel through the water – quicker than through the air. And if the Commander wants to send a message, who am I to disagree? He must have a reason. He must think someone can hear it.'

'But what does it say?'

Jones looked at her suspiciously. 'I couldn't tell you. Even if I knew. That signal is being transmitted in a code that's not in my code book.'

Jones pulled the earmuffs back on to his head and unclipped one of the small metal pegs, fixing it to another key on the board. 'That's a merchant vessel heading out from the Hanseatic coast,' he said. 'Nothing we need to worry about for now.'

'Would you let me listen?' Marina asked. 'I promise I'll be careful. And I won't touch anything. I'll just listen for a moment.'

Jones looked unsure. Marina pulled a mock pleading face. And, just like Edward, Jones gave in. 'But not for long.'

Marina carefully put the funny earmuffs over her ears. All sound was blurred, like when she had slipped under the water in the bath at home. Instead, she could hear her own breathing and it sounded like waves. She sighed. That wasn't very interesting. Was that all she was going to hear – herself? She looked at Jones, who was staring intently at one of the dials. He tapped it with his fingers. 'Do I look funny?' she asked. But she couldn't gauge the volume of her voice and she must have been shouting, because Jones put his finger to his lips and shook his head, vehemently. 'Whoops,' she mouthed.

Marina stared at the dials in front of her. If only Miss Smith could send the *Sea Witch* a message right now. Perhaps she might ask all shipping to look out for her dear friend Marina Denham, with whom she had been hoping to travel back to London, but who had gone missing on the docks at Portsmouth. No. It would be better if Miss Smith sent a message in a code that only Marina could understand, that she would be able to answer without consulting the code books on Jones's shelf. That would make her father realize what an important member of the crew she was. If only she could hear a message that was just for her.

Marina closed her eyes and crossed her fingers. She willed Miss Smith to contact her. Without the distraction of the lights and gauges, she could hear a faint noise – was this the signal that was being sent from the *Sea Witch*? She wanted to catch the sound, but it was like trying to hold water in your hands. She concentrated harder. This message was in code, but she wanted to understand it. And as she listened to the same faint noise, over and over, she fancied that it sounded like a word being repeated. 'Wait,' it said. 'Wait ... Wait ...'

The signal sped through the water, miles and miles

in the blink of an eye, faster even than the torpedoes, those underwater missiles that the new dreadnoughts had been armed with. But where was this word being sent to? Who would be able to hear it? Who would be able to answer it?

No one, of course. The sea was full of fish, not people. What was her father thinking of, making Jones send a signal over and over which no one could answer? Marina would much rather contact Miss Smith and tell her all her adventures.

'Wait . . .' the signal repeated. She was about to pull the headset off, but thought she caught another noise, another part of the message. 'Stay quiet . . .' And then, something more puzzling, that made no sense. 'Your lost pearl . . .'

What a stupid message. If that was even what she heard. Perhaps it was just the buzzing and whirring of the insides of the signals machine.

But just as Marina admitted to herself that Jones had the most boring job in the world, listening to blips and drips of sound, she heard something.

A breath. A note. A snatch of song.

Her throat went tight. Her chest felt as if it were bound with rope. Marina couldn't breathe. She pushed off the listening equipment.

'I just need to . . .' She stumbled a little as she stood up.

'Are you going to be sick?' Jones asked. 'Do you need a bucket?'

'No . . .'

'What's wrong?'

'I thought I heard something.'

'What?'

But how could Marina explain?

Agonized, ragged sobs . . . dark water . . . a space too small to move . . . Torture. It was the sound of torture. She had never once heard any creature being tortured, but she had recognized the sound immediately.

'I just need fresh air.'

14

Marina leant over the side of the *Sea Witch* and watched the streamers of white foam. What had just happened? What had she just heard?

She took a deep breath of air. One thing was clear: she had embarrassed herself in front of Jones. No wonder the navy wouldn't take girls on their boats if just listening to signals made them feel so ill they had to rush out on deck.

'Are you feeling better?' Jones had followed her out. 'You look very pale. Like you've seen a ghost.'

She turned away, embarrassed. She couldn't explain

what she had felt. It would make her look foolish.

'Sorry,' she muttered. 'I just felt a bit sick.'

'It's very stuffy in that room,' he said, looking relieved. 'I'm not good in small spaces either. That's why I couldn't stay down the pit. But as long as I know there's some sky above me, I don't go beserk.'

It was an odd thing to say, Marina thought.

He smiled at her, shy again. 'You sure you're not going to be sick? It's just I can't leave the machine. There's a signal due.'

'I feel much better.' She smiled as brightly as she could. 'And thank you for letting me help you. Even though I wasn't much help.'

'It's nice to have some company.' He shrugged, his cheeks pink from the wind or from his own awkward-ness – it was hard to tell which. 'And we're all members of the crew.'

Members of the crew. That didn't seem like such a simple thing now. She was on a boat, with her father. But where was the boat going, and what was her father going to do? No one had explained and she felt that no one would do so even if she asked.

Boats were going missing in the seas to the north and her father was heading for that very place. Was the *Sea Witch* in danger? And what of that mysterious message he was sending in a secret code? Who was that intended for?

How Marina wished that she could talk to Miss Smith about this: she knew so much about Admiralty business; perhaps she could explain to Marina what the *Sea Witch* was getting tangled up in.

The sun set; the sky flushed pink and the sea answered with its own rosy glow. Marina heard the mournful strain of an accordion and a man's voice singing.

'As I sailed out one day, one day . . .'

The song spiralled out over the water, like smoke.

'And being not far from land,

I spied a mermaid sitting on a rock,

With a comb and a glass in her hand . . .'

Marina closed her eyes as the music lapped around her. It was Brown who sang this sad ballad of sailors who saw a mermaid and knew they would surely drown. They bravely took turns to bid farewell to their loved ones.

'Then up stepped the captain of our ship,

'And a well-speaking man is he.

'He says: 'I have a wife, my boys, in fair Plymouth town,

'But this night and a widow she shall be.'

*

When Marina climbed into her hammock that night, she found no sleep there. The light, pulsing noise of her father's coded signal seemed to reach her even though she wore no listening equipment. She put her hands over her ears, but still it found her.

'I'll get no rest down here,' she said to the dogs as she swung her legs over the side of her hammock and scrambled back up on deck.

Endless waves illuminated by sequins of starlight. They rose and fell, and Marina rose and fell with them. This movement no longer made her feel sick; instead she welcomed each glittering, silver, moonlit wave. The sea spread out around her – another country, another realm, although one that could never fully be conquered, however many warships a king or an archduke might have. Marina frowned as she remembered something her father had told her the day he had left for his boat and this strange mission. He had said there were other ways of commanding the sea, which owed nothing to gunboats. What had he meant by that?

She looked up at the stars; how odd that mariners had needed these tiny specks of light to find their way. Marina closed her eyes and felt that she could just as easily follow that strange, tugging feeling of the currents beneath the waves. But where would they take her?

Perhaps to her mother's country, wherever that unknown place might be.

She turned her head to catch a sound. What was it?

It was coming from behind the lifeboat. A sob. A sniff. Someone cleared their throat.

It is almost impossible to stand where you are and listen to someone struggle with unhappiness, and so Marina went towards the noise.

'Hello?' she said, before stepping behind the lifeboat. 'Don't be alarmed.' It is also hard to intrude on someone else's unhappiness. 'Do you need anything? A glass of water? I could fetch you something to eat?'

A second's silence and then a voice replied, 'No need.'

'Do you feel unwell?'

'No, I'm quite well.' Another sniff.

'Are you sure?'

Jones was bent over the side of the boat. He turned away, embarrassed.

'I'm sorry,' Marina said. 'It's just that I heard you.'

'What are you doing, creeping around on deck after it's time to be in your bed? Listening to people? It's not right!' He sounded defiant, but his voice broke at the end and he hunched his shoulders, trying to stifle another sob. 'Oh, I never thought it would be like this,' he whispered to himself. 'I thought I would be so happy at sea...'

Marina gave him a few moments to get control of himself. A final sniff and he turned to her, blinking.

'I'm fine now,' he said, attempting a smile. 'It's my first trip away from home, see. My first time at sea. I've never been further than Merthyr Tydfil before . . . That's in Wales,' he added, as he saw Marina's confusion. And then he laughed at himself. 'Do you miss home?'

'Oh, no!'

'I suppose it helps that your mother's not around.'

'How would you know that?'

'Brown said you've no mother.'

'She left us...'

'Left you? Where did she go? Oh!' He put his hand to his mouth. 'You mean she...'

'My father said she went home...' Marina explained. 'She was very ill and the London air was not good for her.'

He nodded as if he understood. 'It's just that my mam died last year.' He sniffed again and turned away. 'Sometimes I forget that she's died. And the day seems normal. And then I remember that I'll never see her again, and the sadness and the missing her just comes over me. Like a wave.'

'I was very young when my mother left.'

'So you don't miss her?'

'I don't know. Perhaps. I can't remember very much about her, you see, so I don't know if I can miss what I can't remember.'

'I get worried that I'm forgetting things about my mam. Since I got on the *Sea Witch*, I can't remember her voice. I'd always been able to hear her before. The way she said "Owen" when I came in the house. It was such a kind voice. Everything she said to me just made me feel loved. But now I can't hear her. I can't catch her tone. Oh, I wish I hadn't left home,' he whispered.

'I've never heard my mother's voice,' Marina said, looking out at the sea. 'She couldn't speak, you see.'

Jones looked as if he were trying to smile. 'I wonder what she'd say to you if she saw you now. Dressed in those oilskins.'

'I think she'd say I looked quite wonderful.' Marina laughed.

What would Edward think of Jones, she thought? Would he think the boy would make a good friend? But already Edward seemed a person from another time, or a character out of a book. Not quite real.

'We should get some sleep. You don't want to catch cold,' Jones said, but he was the one shivering, not Marina. She could have stayed on deck all night.

Blowing on his hands, Jones moved away. Marina took one last look at the waves. They seemed so solid, so impenetrable, as if she only had to step on to the water and she could walk wherever she wanted. But where would that be? Where would she go if she had the freedom of the oceans?

Male voices drifted towards them. The speakers came closer, until they stood on the other side of the lifeboat. It felt awkward to climb out from their hiding place now, so Marina and Jones agreed with an exchanged glance to stay where they were.

'Who is this Trenchard, anyway?' they heard Perkins ask.

'Seemed to get his orders last minute,' Brown replied.

'I don't like the look of him. He's surly. Gives you a look as if he'd rather spit on you.'

'He's a good worker, though. So what if he doesn't say much?'

'But what's he thinking?' Perkins asked.

'Leave him be. You'll never know what any man is thinking. And it's probably best you don't.'

'I still don't like it, Brown. We're in an old fishing

boat fitted with the engine of a gunboat. We're going north when there's a war about to break out. And to that cursed island. We thought we'd never get off it the last time we was there. I've got a funny feeling about this mission.'

'Well, you can keep your funny feelings to yourself and get on with your work. The Commander knows what he's doing, and that's good enough for me.'

'But what is he doing?'

'There's some signals equipment – a sonar transmitter or something – that's been left up on Pechorin Island. Needs mending before the war starts. That's what I heard the Commander tell Finchin.'

'That blasted island. That's where I nearly lost my finger from frostbite. That winter was so cold. Why are we the ones to go back?'

'Because orders is orders. And we're navy men. And we're the best of the navy men, which is why they've sent us.'

'That's true enough.' Perkins sighed. 'We're the best they've got. But still, I wish they'd found some other poor sailors to send that way instead of us.'

'Aye, but maybe we'll find you a pretty girl up there to bring home with you . . . She could sing you a lullaby . . .'

The voices moved away until only the sound of the waves was left.

'Did you know about that?' Marina asked Jones.

'The sonar transmitter on the island?' He frowned. 'I didn't. But it makes sense. Your father is the best signals man the navy has got. If they need something mending, they'd send him.'

'But why do the navy need a sonar transmitter on an island in the middle of nowhere?'

'The Mordavians have started moving their battle-ships north. They're going to block the passage to the New World colonies. The British can't let that happen. The war will start with a battle in the Sea of Murmansk. The Admiralty must need that transmitter to send orders to their boats. Your father's mission may change the outcome of the war.'

Could this be true, Marina wondered. If it was so important, why had Miss Smith had no knowledge of it?

Jones hugged himself. 'This wind,' he shivered. 'I feel like it could blow up a storm.'

They bid each other goodnight, but as Marina climbed down into the hold, she saw a small spot of red light floating in the air. She ducked down and watched as a dark figure appeared. Trenchard, smoking. He paced from one side of the boat to the other, back and forth, always looking over the side.

As if he were searching for something in the black, impenetrable water.

15

The next morning, as Marina climbed up from the hold in answer to the clanging of the mess bell, she saw something which made her lower the hatch so that she could peer out unobserved. A small fishing net had been dropped in the night. Brown, Perkins and Trenchard were standing a few feet away from her, inspecting the catch.

'Is it alive?' Brown was bending over the tangled net.

'Nah, mate. Look at its eyes!' Perkins replied. 'I'd not get too close, though.'

'We should throw it back in.' Brown stood up. 'It's giving me the collywobbles.'

'It's a sea witch,' Trenchard declared.

'Hush man,' Brown hissed.

'Why? We all know what it is. Probably called up by the girl.'

'Hush, man! She's only a child.'

'Use your eyes. You've been at sea for years and never seen anything like this,' Trenchard needled. 'But that *girl* is on the boat for just *days* and look what gets caught in our net.'

'That's no way to talk about the Commander's daughter,' Perkins said, shocked.

'Yeah. You wind your neck in, Trenchard,' Brown growled. 'You've got one of your moods on you.' He squared up to him. He was the shorter man, but broader. 'No more talk about the girl and sea witches, or you'll be the one going overboard.'

Trenchard shrugged his shoulders into his heavy duffel coat and stepped back. 'You'll be sorry you didn't listen to me. There's no good comes of letting girls on boats.' He took himself off to the mess.

'Nothing but a troublemaker, that one,' Brown said. 'As if there are sea witches and strange creatures under the sea!'

Perkins shivered and pulled his knitted cap further down over his ears. 'I wouldn't be too sure,' he said. 'Did

131

you know my grandfather saw a mermaid once? He heard a singing and a great sadness came over his heart. Thought it would sink him. And then he looks up and he sees her, sitting on a rock in the moonlight. Her skin was pale and her eyes were like dark pools a man could drown in. She was the most beautiful thing he'd ever seen.'

'Was she combing her hair?'

'Aye, she was that.'

'And did she have a fish's tail?'

'Aye. With scales made from starlight.' Perkins sighed.

Brown pushed him towards the mess. 'Get over! Stop talking rot! Let's get some food in you. We can deal with the catch after breakfast.'

Marina crept out. She edged towards the net. What was the thing they had seen? Amongst the shining, mercury-coloured fishes, she saw a tangle of tentacles. She crept closer. She mustn't be scared – the creature was dead. But as she bent over it, it twitched and uncoiled a limb, which it flicked around her ankle, as if asking for her help. Its eyelid drew back and revealed a large glassy eye. The eye looked not just at her, but into her. It made her think of her experience in the Signals Room the day before: how she had felt as if she were hearing someone being hurt or punished. She shuddered. Well, here was a creature she could help.

'Wait,' she whispered, as she bent over the net. 'Wait . . .' And she gently pulled the creature out of the pile of fish. She thought it would feel slimy, and held her breath when she slid her fingers beneath it, but the creature's skin was smooth and cool, like a pearl. It was far heavier than she had imagined, with its large head and many limbs. She could see its heart still beating through the semi-transparent flesh. And still its eye observed her, patiently, trusting that Marina would soon give it its freedom. She carried it over to the side of the boat and threw it into the water. It floated for an instant, like blossom and sea foam mixed, and then sank into the depths below.

After breakfast, Marina was surprised when Brown whispered for her to stay behind. 'I've got something to say to the Commander,' he explained. 'And I think you need to hear it.'

He cleared his throat. 'Sir! Permission to speak, sir.'

Commander Denham nodded his assent. 'What is it, Brown?'

'Sir. I had a thought about how Miss De— I mean, the Boy—'

'2nd Class,' Finchin interrupted.

'The Boy, 2nd Class,' Brown repeated. 'I had a thought about how she – I mean, he – might be helpful, sir.'

'You had a thought?' Finchin enquired. 'I don't recall that we pay you to have thoughts, Brown.'

'It's a good one, though, sir.' Brown cleared his throat and addressed the Commander. The words that followed gave the impression that he had practised them many times over. 'I've always been a good worker, and been proud to be on every voyage you've taken for the Admiralty. You've got us into some fair old scrapes, Commander, but you've always got us out again. But when I sign up for your missions, sir, I sign up as an Able Seaman. With respect, sir, I do not sign up for the chopping of meat for the dogs and the changing of straw in the dogs' crate.'

'Ah,' Finchin commented. 'Now we're getting to the heart of the matter.'

'All right, Finchin,' Commander Denham said. 'Let's hear the man out.'

'I was wonderin' if, sir . . .'

'You want another member of the crew to take over some of your duties?'

Marina's heart jumped. 'Oh, Father!' she gasped. 'I mean, Commander, sir. Do please let me.'

Her father gave the request some thought. 'What do you think, Finchin?'

'It might work, sir. And it's better to have the crew working well together. And we don't seem to have found any way of harnessing the young seaman's, uh, talents.'

'Well, Boy, 2nd Class. You've always wanted an occupation. Now you've got one. You can look after those eight dogs. They need to be kept in good condition, mind. They need fresh straw and clean water every day. And exercise. They will need to run for eighteen hours at a stretch once I reach the ice. And they will be dragging a sledge. So you can't fuss over them. They are working animals, not pets. I can't stress enough just how important those animals are to the success of my mission. I could lose almost anything on this boat. But without those dogs . . .'

'I'll do a good job, sir. I will! Just watch me! I won't let you down.'

Marina jumped down the steps into the hold.

'Greetings, subjects,' she laughed. She struck what she hoped was a regal pose. 'I am now your queen and you must swear your allegiance to me. I'll have no traitors here! You must all do my bidding!'

135

If by 'bidding' she meant tail-thumping and yowl-ing, then the dogs were happy to oblige.

She knelt down next to the crate. The dogs barked fit to burst and tried to push their faces through the bars. She took a deep breath and put her hand out to let them all sniff her. She laughed at their cold noses, their warm breath and their daft enthusiasm.

'I'll have to give you names,' she said, 'otherwise this is going to get very complicated.'

But what names should she choose? The kings of the Old Testament? That strutting grey one could be Nebuchadnezzar. But she was stuck, then, because she couldn't remember any more. Perhaps they could be named after Greek heroes. 'You can be Achilles,' she said, pointing at the one with the grey patch on his face. 'And you can be Milo.' But then she felt bad because those heroes never seemed to come to a decent end. She didn't like to think of Achilles' fluffy paw with a spear in it. Or Milo's body torn apart by wolves. No! As she looked into each kind, intelligent dog's face, she thought she would give them the names of friends she might have made if she had gone to Edward's school.

'You are Gerald,' she said to one with startling blue eyes. 'No point barking like that: you are definitely a Gerald.' She pointed at the next fluffy head. 'You're a

George, and no mistake. You have to be Jeremy.' The dog howled his approval. 'You! Don't turn your head away! You're Richard.' She stopped for a moment, frowning. What other names would suit these dogs? 'Oscar, William, Monty.' She laughed at the last one, because he really did suit that name. 'And *you* . . .' She looked at the dog with the odd-coloured eyes. 'You look like you are in charge, so you can be called Patrick,' she whispered, tapping him on the nose. He put his head on one side and observed her with one sky-blue eye and one brown. 'But I will call you Paddy.'

She let them out of their crate and watched them run around in the hold. They sniffed and investigated and busied about. But she knew she would have to find a better way to exercise such powerful creatures if they were to be used to pull a loaded sledge in freezing conditions for hours at a time.

Marina forked the dogs' dirty straw into a net, just as she had seen Brown do. Then she took it up on deck and emptied it over the side into the sea. She spread clean straw for them. 'Doesn't that smell nice?' she told them.

She sat in her hammock, watching them. Paddy went to the bottom of the steps and yowled. 'Do you want to go out?' she asked. 'Is that what you're telling me?'

Perhaps she could run the dogs round the deck? That should keep them fit and ready for their mission.

She took her length of rope out of the pocket of her oilskins. Paddy came and sat at her feet and watched as she undid the knots. 'Do you see? This one is very difficult. It won't take a second . . .' (It took rather longer and involved Marina's teeth.) 'Now, I'm going to invent a knot that is very good for tying round dogs' necks,' she told him. She made something like a loose slipknot and pushed it over Paddy's ears. 'It will be called the Paddy knot and it will go down in history as the best knot ever invented!'

She put the rest of the dogs in the crate and told them – in strict, ringing tones – to wait their turn. And then she half-dragged Paddy up on deck. Hopefully her father would still be on the bridge and he would see how hard she was working.

Paddy sniffed the air. He seemed unsure now that he was on deck that this was where he wanted to be. He voiced his concerns about the height of the swell. The wind ruffled his deep fur.

'Now, Paddy. There's no point complaining. We all need a walk in the fresh air!' That was what Ivy told her when she had pies to make and wanted to be left alone.

'We are going to be such a good team,' she went on. 'The Commander will be so pleased with us.' Maybe she could get the dogs so fit that they could run for twenty hours a day!

Paddy yowled uncertainly as the boat pitched.

'Let's keep moving,' Marina said. She jogged across the deck, pulling Paddy along. He began to look more confident. And in fact, could run very quickly. Rather too quickly. 'Steady on,' she cried. 'You've got four legs and I've only got two.'

Brown and Perkins were nowhere to be seen. What a shame. Still, she had another seven dogs to put through their paces, so they might still see how good she was at her job. And Jones was coming out of the Signals Room. At last, here was someone she could impress with how hard she could work.

16

Feeling very pleased with herself, Marina ran Paddy across the deck again. The waves smashed about the prow, the spray soaked them both, but she felt that only made her dedication and her efforts more impressive. But Jones didn't seem remotely interested in her or in Paddy.

'I'm just putting this dog through his paces,' she called out.

Perhaps Jones couldn't hear her, because he said nothing, leaning over the side of the boat and staring into the water.

'Are you feeling all right?' Marina asked him, wiping

seawater from her face. 'I thought you weren't meant to leave the signals machine?'

'The Commander is in the Signals Room,' Jones said to the waves. 'He's not in a good mood. The machine is not working properly. He probably thinks I broke it.' He bit his lip, blinked away tears, or the wind – Marina couldn't be sure. 'Oh, don't worry. I didn't tell him I let you use it. That would have sent him into a dreadful mood, and he's bad enough as it is.' Jones shook his head. 'I don't think the machine is broken. I think something is jamming the signal. But the Commander won't listen to me: he says there's nothing for miles around that could jam anything. And I just don't see why that coded message is so important.'

'Jones?' Marina's father called from the door of the Signals Room.

'Sir!'

'Get in here! I need help with the transponder!'

The waves rose up. Marina decided to get Paddy back in the hold. She pulled him along. But Paddy tensed, his thick fur bristling, his head lifted to the sky. He growled.

'Paddy!' She tapped him on the nose. 'Manners, please.' His ears were flat against his head. His growl got deeper and more hostile. 'What are you trying to tell me?'

An arc of black in the sky. She just caught it before it was lost behind the crest of a rising wave, but as the water fell, it reappeared.

'You big silly,' Marina said. She pulled the dog closer, held him tightly to her chest. 'It's just a *bird*.'

She screwed up her eyes against the salt spray. Viewed this way, the bird looked as if it were dragging the fleet of steel-grey clouds towards the boat.

'Stop growling, Paddy. You've seen birds before.'

But never a bird like this, warned Paddy's insistent growl.

The creature flew very low over the water, rising and falling above the waves, always keeping the same distance between its wings and the water. Unlike the herring gulls with their raucous screeching, this bird was silent.

Perkins stopped his work and stared up at it.

'Oi!' Brown shouted, looking up from the rope he was coiling. 'No daydreaming.'

'Have you seen that?' Perkins indicated the bird with a nod of his head.

Brown looked up. He dropped the rope and walked purposefully to the side of the boat. Paddy started growling again.

'What is that?' Marina heard Brown say.

'It's . . . It's not an albatross, is it?' Perkins had dropped his broom and joined Brown. They both stared up the bird.

'There's none of them in these skies,' Brown said. 'They're southern birds. You know that. And their plumes is white.'

'But what else would be flying this far out from land and staying so close to the boat?' Perkins asked, his voice anxious.

'If you don't like the look of it, just get rid of it.'

'And how am I going to do that? Climb up on the winch? You know I can't stand heights. When I was a boy and we still had sailing ships, they had to send someone else up the rigging to trim the sails. I couldn't do it.'

'Well I'm not climbing up to get it. I've got a bad hip!' And Brown clutched his waist and pulled a face.

'First I've heard of it,' Perkins grumbled. 'Urgh. That bird gives me the collywobbles.' Perkins was still looking at it. 'I'm afeared it will peck my eyes out.'

'It's only come to say hello,' Brown jeered. 'Look, it's coming closer. Coming to say hello to you and take a nibble of them eyeballs.'

Perkins backed away. 'I'm going to tell the

143

Commander about it.'

'And what's he going to do? Other than tell you you're a complete ninny!'

'I tell you, I don't like the look of the thing. It's . . . it's . . . malevolent! It's a bird of ill omen!'

Brown went back to his work. But he, too, seemed bothered by the bird, looking up, uneasy. Marina felt that if she could just get up high enough, she could swipe it right out of the air. The bird seemed to be taunting her, flying close to the boat and yet keeping the tip of its wings just out of reach.

'They all think I'm useless,' she whispered to Paddy. 'But there's something that I can do that they can't. I can climb!'

She glanced up at the bridge. Finchin was bent over his sea charts. Brown was hauling a heavy coil of rope. She would have two minutes, three at most. She just had to get up on to the winch without alerting the bird to her plan.

Were there enough hand-holds? Where would she put her feet? She looked at the winch with a practised climber's eye. She didn't want to get halfway and get stuck. She calculated her ascent quickly. She could just about do it.

Her foot slipped off at her first attempt – a trail of

thick grease applied too generously. But now she had her footing. She grasped the large metal pin with her right hand, put her left foot on the bolt. Her left hand reached up for the bracket, wet with seawater. She hauled her body up. She swung one leg over the winch arm. The *Sea Witch* tilted as it crested a wave. Marina was thrown backwards, but caught herself in time. She lay along the winch, holding tight with both arms. The trick would be to wait until the bird was close enough and she could risk taking one hand off. She should be frightened – this was not like climbing a tree. A gulp of sea air. Her legs soaked by a wave. But she only had to be brave for another minute and then she would have the wing of that malevolent bird. Up close, it was much smaller than she had thought – the size of a large crow. She straightened up, reached out her hand. Just a little further.

The sea below. How deep was it? Could it be as deep as it was wide? How long would it take to sink to the bottom? Hours? Days? Years? It was best not to think.

Paddy's bark of alarm.

'Oi! What you doing?' Brown's startled cry.

She mustn't look down. Mustn't look round, even though she could hear another man's shout. 'They must learn to be braver,' Marina whispered to herself, quite calm. 'They must learn that girls are every bit as much use as boys.'

She lunged forward, fingers outstretched. 'I've got it!' she cried in triumph.

There was an odd sound, like a hiss of steam. The bird flew on, as if unaware that she had it by the wing. It was dragging her with it.

She would have to let go, or her arm would be torn from its socket.

An odd, sick feeling in her stomach. Waves became clouds as she slipped underneath the winch. She clung on with both legs, one arm wrapped around the winch arm. She still had the bird in the other; its strength, though, was terrifying as it strained to be free.

How could she climb back up with the bird in her hand?

How long could she hang on with one arm?

Her leg slipped, a wave caught her hair, and she fell, the black sea closing over her head.

17

The first seconds she lost all sense of her weight, of her body, of how quickly she was falling through the dark, cold water. It was pressing in on her from all sides, squeezing the air out of her. How much longer would it take before she drowned?

But I have been in the sea before. It was an odd thought to have, especially when she should be panicking, when she should be trying to kick her legs and get up to the surface.

Her mother's green silk skirt set out in a circle around her on the beach. It had been warm that day. Marina wore a sun bonnet. She reached out her little hands to play with the ropes of pearls that hung from her mother's throat. Her mother – her face so beautiful, with those large emerald eyes and trailing black hair – smiled down at Marina, who now reached up to wind the pearls round her chubby wrists. Her mother bent down and kissed her lightly on the tip of her nose. And then she was clutched tight against her mother's silk dress, the pearls pressed into her face. Her mother was wading into the sea, the green dress floating behind her like a seaweed garden. The sea! It splashed up into Marina's face, cold and salty. 'Mama!' Marina cried out, shocked by the chill droplets on her skin. And then she roared as an icy wave caught her foot. But still her mother plunged forward, holding Marina so tightly that she couldn't wriggle free, however hard she tried. Her father's startled cry. Her mother stopped, waist-deep in water, as if turned to coral.

Her father's arms had taken her from her mother's tight embrace, she was sure. But where was her father now? He couldn't follow her here, fathoms down in the dark cold water. He couldn't save her.

She heard a low thrumming noise and, through her hair, which streamed across her face, she saw a great black shape, like a giant bug, scudding through the water.

Before it could get to her, a mesh of ropes closed around her . . . And Marina realized that she had not been at all frightened until that moment. But these ropes clawed at her hair and her face; they fastened themselves around her neck, her legs, her arms. She tried to kick free, but that made their grip even more deadly. She had to be free of them if she was to breathe. The ropes would drown her, not the sea – *they* would stop her breathing, not the embrace of the deep, dark, all-encompassing water. She was trapped. It was unbearable . . . to be caught like this . . . in the net . . . ropes tightening around her throat and chest. Impossible . . . to brea—

'Is she breathing?'

'She can't be. She was under for too long.'

'We'll have to tell the Commander. How will we tell the Commander? We'll get it in the neck from the Commander.'

'Finchin's gone to get him.'

Marina opened her eyes. What did she see? Clouds billowing above. Two shocked faces bent over her. Brown and Perkins looked so comical that she started to laugh.

Paddy nudged her face with his nose and then licked it with his rough, cool tongue.

'Out of my way, man.' The Commander pulled Perkins back by the shoulder. His face was drawn and white. Marina felt very sorry that her father looked so anxious, so scared.

She felt his arms beneath her shoulder blades and legs. She was lifted up, and felt the water running out of her oilskins. Her father walked smartly towards his quarters. Finchin, just ahead of him, opened the door and stepped aside as Marina was carried in. It was all as quick and smooth as if it had been rehearsed many times.

'Blankets!' her father called. 'And a hot kettle. She'll need something warm to drink. And dry clothes, too.' He pulled off her boot and seawater belched on to the floor.

'We might need a mop,' Marina said.

But her father seemed unable to speak to her. He pulled off her oilskins, wrapped her in blankets, and then took her hands in his palms and rubbed them vigorously. Only once he was sure that her hands were quite warm could he bring himself to speak.

'How did this happen?' he said. 'What were you thinking?'

Finchin returned with more blankets and an enamel mug, which he handed to Marina. Steam rose up. The smell made her wrinkle her nose. 'Drink it,' he said, sounding stern instead of his usual affable self. 'It's an order.'

Marina took a tentative sip. 'Urgh. It makes my throat burn,' she spluttered.

Her father stared at her. 'Are you cold? Is anything broken?'

'I bashed my elbow,' Marina answered. 'And my leg.' Her shoulder was what really hurt, but she didn't want to worry him.

'Finchin? Get Brown and Perkins in here!'

'They had nothing to do with this, Fath—'

'Not another word,' the Commander warned.

The men were fetched. They looked awkward, downcast, fidgeting in the doorway. They couldn't give an easy account of how their Commander's only child had ended up in the sea.

'One minute she was on deck—' Perkins started.

'And then she was up on the winch,' Brown interrupted. 'No warning. Nothing. I couldn't believe my eyes. And she's just reaching out for that blooming bird. My heart was in my mouth, Commander. I couldn't speak nor anything. She gave me such a fright.'

'But we got the nets out real quick when she fell in,' Perkins said.

'We could see her the whole time she was under the water,' Brown chipped in. 'Her eyes were open. Staring at us.'

'We caught her in the net. Like a fish.'

'All right. All right.' The Commander rubbed his brow. When he spoke again, his voice was less harsh. 'Thank you, men. I'm grateful to you. Your quick thinking and quick actions saved my daughter's life.'

'It's no trouble, Commander. No sailor likes to see one of his own overboard,' Brown croaked.

'We're just pleased she's still breathing,' Perkins said, peering intently at Marina.

The Commander dismissed them and they shuffled off, although Perkins could not resist one last, puzzled look at Marina.

'What were you thinking?' Her father tucked a wet tendril of hair behind her ear. 'Although I'd wager you weren't thinking at all. You're so—'

'Impulsive. I know. Edward told me.'

'When I heard you'd gone overboard, I thought . . .' He clutched her to him. She winced in pain but bit her lip rather than cry out. 'After everything I've done over the years to keep you safe. To lose you to the sea would be unbearable,' he whispered in her ear.

A knock on the open door. Finchin had returned.

He looked grave. 'You gave us quite a scare, Marina. But I'm glad to see no harm's been done. That sea is pretty cold. You must be a lot sturdier than we gave you credit for.'

'I don't feel the cold,' Marina said, taking another sip of the fiery drink. 'I'm tough as old boots.'

'That you are,' Finchin replied, a smile flickering on his lips. 'Although a little headstrong.' He raised an eyebrow. 'Chip off the old block, if you don't mind my saying, sir.'

'I do mind.'

Finchin cleared his throat and held up a limp, feathered shape. 'Sir . . . I found this on deck. The seabird that gave Perkins such a fright. It was in the net. With Marina.'

'I didn't let it go!' Marina cried. 'I had him so tight by the wing I thought he'd pull my arm off.' The hot brandy had loosened her tongue, and her wits, too, if the expressions on her father's and Finchin's face were anything to go by.

'Get rid of the thing, Finchin. Why do I want a dead bird on my ship? Especially if Perkins is going to get into one of his funny moods.'

'Well, that's just the thing, sir. It isn't a bird.'

He handed the mass of feathers to the Commander.

The neck looked as if it were broken, and indeed the head came away from the body as the men exchanged the strange catch.

'What the—'

'Exactly, sir.'

'What is it?'

'It looks as if it's some sort of airborne signals device, sir. It's done up to look like a bird, but if you peel the feathers back – they're sewn on to a leather skin – you'll see a box inside the cavity. You can still hear it whirring. The seawater hasn't affected it. You can clearly see the stamp of the factory where it was made.'

The Commander peered into the bird's body. 'Ah.'

'Exactly. The Mordavian Telegraph Factory.' He smiled at Marina. 'I have to hand it to the Mordavians, sir. This is way beyond anything our chaps have come up with – or could come up with. Not only have they suspended a box that heavy in the air from such a small wingspan, but they've kept it there for the time it has taken to fly from the coast.'

'This is what has been interfering with my signals equipment.'

'Not any longer, sir. I took the liberty of pulling that wire out of its alternator. It won't cause any more harm.'

'Get Jones in here.'

'Sir.' Finchin stepped outside and banged on the Signals Room door.

The Commander took the box out of the fake bird's body and turned it over in his hands. He seemed entranced. He slid open a panel on the side. It was tightly packed with small metal cogs and wheels, which ticked like a watch mechanism. 'Such a delicate instrument,' he breathed in wonder. 'See these?' He tilted the box to show Marina two small glass phials of coloured liquid linked by copper wires to a tiny pressure gauge. 'This blue one is a gas called sentium. The silver is philium. Even a thimbleful, when mixed, could keep this machine in the air for years. It's so simple, and yet it's never been done before.'

'Why not?' Marina was fascinated by the whirring of the cogs. Behind them a small leather pouch inflated and emptied like a lung.

'Those gases are very rare. There's only one place in the world where they exist.'

Finchin coughed. Marina looked up to see Jones's shocked face. Of course. He would have had his listening equipment on and would not have known what had happened to her.

'Jones. Get on to Room 40. Don't worry, we've solved the problem of the signal being jammed. Send them a message using the Nephilim code. It's in your code book, only move all the settings to the left two spaces. Can you handle that?'

Jones nodded. He looked tense. 'What should I say, sir?'

'Tell them we've got hold of a Mordavian airborne signals device. And insist that the Admiralty launch their own top-secret Valkyrie equipment.'

'Sir.'

When he had left, Finchin looked worried. 'The Nephilim code, sir? I thought the Mordavians had cracked that one two days ago.'

'That's correct.'

'But this Valkyrie airborne equipment –' he looked puzzled – 'do we want to be telling them about it?'

'Yes we do! Especially as we don't actually have any such equipment, Finchin. And we're not likely to. Even if we could keep something in the air, we'd never be able to power it for long enough for it to get past a lighthouse, let alone into the North Sea. But we might as well let the Mordavians think we do.'

'I like your play, Commander. It's not cricket, of course . . .'

'It's war, Finchin. Or it will be soon.'

The Commander stood up and signalled to his First

Officer to follow him outside. The door was still ajar. Marina hopped out of bed to listen to them.

'How long was she in the sea?' her father asked. 'Brown's surely got confused. He thinks she was in the water for quite a while. They had to get the net fixed to the winch and let it down into the sea. They could see her the entire time, he says. Perkins insisted that her eyes were open, staring up at them.'

'Both of them have been wittering on,' Finchin replied. 'All gibberish, as far as I can make out.'

'Did Trenchard see anything?'

'He wasn't on deck.'

'Give them all double rations of rum. That should calm them quick enough.'

'Sir. Do you think it's time we looked again at this mission?'

'What do you mean?'

'If that device has been following us, sir, and jamming the coded signal from your machine – well, it must mean that Mordavian Intelligence know where we are. We've lost our element of surprise, sir.'

'We're not turning round, Finchin.'

'I understand your reluctance, Commander, bu—'

'No ifs or buts, Finchin. We're going north.'

Marina jumped back under the blankets. She closed

her eyes as the door swung open.

'Tired, eh?' the Commander said as he sat next to her.

'Not really.' She didn't want her father to go. 'I'm so sorry, Father,' she whispered. 'I've put you to an awful lot of trouble.'

'But you're safe now. And that's all that matters.'

'When I was under the water—'

'Shhhhh . . .' He stroked her damp hair.

'It was the strangest thing. I had a memory that I had been to the seaside. When I was very little.' She searched her father's face as she said this, looking for any telltale sign that he recalled the seaside too. His face looked gentle and kind but showed no recollection of the day. 'I remem—'

'Or thought you did . . .'

'Or I thought I did,' she corrected herself, although she was sure that it was a real memory, 'that Mama carried me into the sea. And just as I remembered this, I saw a large black shape in the water, coming quickly towards me . . .'

Her father was smiling now, but in a kindly way, as if she had said something very foolish. 'But what could you see down there, Marina? It's too dark to see anything.'

'I . . . I don't know what it was. But it was big. And so

black. And it was travelling through the water so very fast, as if it wanted to catch me.'

He shook his head. 'You weren't in the water for long enough to see anything.' That calm, rational way her father had of saying things which made her doubt herself.

'Perhaps,' Marina muttered. It did sound unlikely when said aloud. 'You're probably right.'

'Of course I am,' the Commander whispered. He leant over and kissed Marina very gently on the forehead.

Marina's eyelids fluttered. She suddenly felt bone-tired. She tried to conjure up the day at the seaside. 'I wish, just once, Mama might have spoken to me. I know her voice was gone, but . . .'

'And what would you have wanted her to say to you?'

In Marina's imagined meetings, her mother would never say, 'I love you.' The vision Marina conjured up – pale face, dark hair and a throat roped in pearls – always refused, looking troubled and turning her head away. She would only say one word. But that word, which Marina heard resonating inside her – for, of course, her mother had no voice – made her feel loved and understood.

It was just this one word – her name – which she wished her mother had spoken to her.

Marina's head felt heavy, her thoughts draped in a thick sea mist. Her eyelids drooped. It was such a comfort to lie here and feel her father's hand stroke the top of her head. The pillows were so soft, the bed so warm and comfortable. She would tell him. She would tell him . . .

18

The next three days at sea were perhaps the happiest days Marina had spent in her life. Her father – relieved she had not drowned – forgave her impulsive behaviour. He smiled at her quite openly in front of his crew and enquired after her good health. Was she hungry? Did she have enough blankets? But more warming than this obvious care for her physical wellbeing was the way he looked at her. Marina felt that when her father's sharp, intelligent eyes rested on her, they really *saw* her, instead of sliding over her as if she were of no more interest than a chair.

The men, too, behaved more kindly towards her and

included her more in their tasks: Finchin invited her on to the bridge and gave her lessons in navigation. Jones asked for help taking notes on his code book and asked her to test him on the various call signals he used. Her father came in to test the strength of the call signal and declared it excellent, thanking them both for their hard work. When there were no signals to decode, Marina and Jones played word games and puzzles. And if Perkins and Brown sometimes looked at her strangely while she helped them to wind up the winch or fold away the nets, they were not unkind. Only Trenchard's manner was unchanged. But he kept himself to himself. If he was the spy on the boat, there was nothing very much to inform the Admiralty about. Even Marina's foot had stopped itching since she had fallen into the sea.

Marina finally felt that she was a valuable member of the crew of the *Sea Witch*: she attacked her chores with enthusiasm and good humour, revelling in being on deck with the dogs as much as possible.

The weather held fair; the sea – which had seemed so impenetrable, as if forged from metal, or carved from basalt– looked, since her accident, as soft and welcoming as a well-made bed. To her father's surprise, she had not caught a cold in the freezing water. In fact, she felt invigorated, as if the sea had been a health-giving draught. Ivy could put away her ghastly cod liver oil. From now on, Marina would just drink seawater!

It was morning. She had risen early, as usual. She had had no more seasickness since she had tumbled into the sea, and felt stronger and more energetic than ever before. The waves had fallen away as they approached the coast of Finnmark, and the Arctic sun was low in the sky, hazy and blurred through misty clouds. Marina breathed in the sharp, salty air and felt as if she were quite alone on the sea; instead of feeling lonely, she just felt more herself than ever.

She heard the men start their day, saw Trenchard, sullen as ever, move a heavy coil of rope. But as she turned back to look at the sea and the far-distant coast, she saw something that was so unexpected and so shocking that she cried out in alarm.

'What is it, Miss Marina?' Brown called. He was at her side in seconds, clearly worried that she might come to harm. She couldn't speak, was quite silenced by what she had seen. She pointed and at that moment, a column of water spouted out of the sea on an impatient blast of air. A second later a grey dome breached the water, curved like a wave, and was submerged.

'Aye, Miss Marina.' Brown sighed. 'I never get tired of the sight of 'em.'

'Of what?' she asked. Why wasn't he worried? Whatever that *thing* was, it could surely finish off the *Sea Witch* and all who sailed on her as easily as a starving man eating a tin of pilchards.

'It's the whales, miss,' he chuckled. 'On their way to their winter quarters. They've swum for hundreds of miles and they've got hundreds more to go. Look –' he squinted – 'the mother has brought her calf.'

'They won't eat us?'

'Eat us? Why would they want to do that? The whales are far too busy to bother with us, and I don't think we'd make much of a meal for them. They have far more cause to be frightened of us than we of them.'

'Because they are hunted,' Marina replied sadly. She watched the mother whale rise again, blowing air and water into the trembling air.

'Aye, they are. And it is an 'orrible business. The sea is turned red with their blood.' Brown shook his head. 'We're barbarians to do that to such noble creatures. Why do we think we're so clever if all we can do with our intelligence is hunt whales and build warships and guns? I look at those whales and it's like watching the angels dance. And I reckon those whales are more holy, and their prayers and hymns more beautiful, than any hosanna you'd hear in church.' He smiled awkwardly. 'Only don't tell Perkins I said that. He's got more religion than me.'

They watched for a few more moments in companionable silence.

The Commander joined them, not commenting on two of his crew being quite idle. Marina could see how he, too, was hypnotized by the beauty of the creatures.

'Father? Could I ask Jones to come and see them?'

He gave permission with a nod, and Marina went and hammered on Jones's cabin door, telling him to get up and get on deck, 'Quick sharp and no hanging about.'

'But why?' The sleepy voice didn't sound as if it thought anything was worth getting out of a warm berth for.

'You'll see.' And, delighted, Marina ran back to her spot on deck.

Her father was up on the bridge and Brown had returned to his work. She watched the whales alone. And as she stood there, she fancied she could send some part of herself down into the water and hear, in the echoing cavern of the sea through which the animals moved, something astonishing. The mother was singing – in some ancient, wordless language – to her calf, and the calf understood the ocean through its mother's voice.

All of this Marina grasped, without being able to articulate it very clearly to herself. She understood not in her mind, the way she was meant to understand multiplication or French verb endings. She grasped the meaning in her body, as a feeling, as if she were a bell being struck.

Marina took one last look at the whales. There was a language of joy and kindness and creation, somewhere in the world, she was sure. But where was it to be found? Perhaps it had got lost. Or perhaps no one else but she knew of its existence. *I will look for it*, she told herself. *Even if it takes my whole life to find it and another whole life to learn it*. She would go anywhere, follow the whales in their endless progress through their watery worlds. *I'll find that lost language of truth . . .* The water shivered where the whales had dived and she followed them in her imagination. *I'll journey through the lost seas, too. I'll learn to live without air, without light, dive deeper than anyone has ever been. I'll find those precious words that can make a different sort of world and pluck them like pearls from the drowned depths of the ancient, sunless sea.*

19

Gulls screeched a raucous welcome to the *Sea Witch* as she sailed into Svengejar, the most northerly port in the Grand Duchy of Finnmark.

Marina and Jones had been up at first light, excited to see land after so many days at sea. The boat slid into port, leaving streamers of white lace on the surface of the shallow green water of the harbour.

Marina leant right over the side of the boat. 'The sea is like my mother's dress,' she whispered. She reached out her hand as if to stroke the water. It looked just like moiré silk ruffles. 'She always wore green. At least I think so.'

'That's one of the things I'm frightened of,' Jones said, quietly.

'Green dresses?'

'No.' He elbowed her. 'Forgetting. Not being able to remember how my mam smoothed her apron or how she tied her shawl. Her fingers were always so red and sore.'

'You won't forget.' But Marina had – if she'd ever known.

'But the more I think about her, the harder it is to hold the memory fresh in my mind.'

As they spoke, the water became agitated, as if it were being stirred from below.

'Do you think there are creatures down there?' Marina asked Jones. It was a foolish thing to ask, but she suddenly wanted to know what he thought.

'Of course there are!'

'But . . . like us?'

Jones turned to face her. It had been a mistake to say anything, she knew. 'Are you touched in the head or something?' he asked.

'It's just that there was something in the nets . . . Something that didn't look like a fish. Trenchard said it was a sea witch . . .'

'All sorts come up from the deep. We can't know everything.'

'Perkins said his grandfather had seen a mermaid. And Brown sings that song about how the mermaid sings a boat to the deep.'

'There's lots of sailors say they've seen mermaids . . .'

'But do you think they exist?'

'I don't suppose so. Any more than unicorns or dragons. I mean, if dragons did really fly around stealing gold and breathing fire, someone would have seen them by now.'

'They'd be pretty hard to miss.' Marina laughed. She stared harder at the sea and the patterns being made by the *Sea Witch*'s progress. 'I wish mermaids did exist,' she whispered.

'Why?'

'Because I think that I could swim with one . . . What? Why are you laughing?'

'You? Swim? That didn't go very well for you the last time you went in the water!'

'But they'd give me a magic shell or something that would mean that I could breathe underwater. Wouldn't you want to swim through the endless, infinite oceans? With a mermaid? Perkins's grandfather said they are very beautiful. The one he saw was sitting on a rock, combing her hair.'

Jones shuddered. 'Remember, Marina. I didn't want

to go down the mines. I like breathing air and looking at the sky! I'm not interested in listening to mermaids singing their sad songs. They're no friends to sailors. They're dangerous company.'

'I don't care! I want to swim with the mermaids and follow the path the sea is showing me.' During the days she had spent on the *Sea Witch*, Marina had had a creeping feeling that if she could just find a way of understanding the sea, its moods and its movement, it would take her where she wanted to go. She shook her head. It was all very confusing and sounded silly now she'd tried to say it out loud.

Jones stared at her, astonished. 'The only path you'll find with that attitude is down to the bottom of the ocean!'

'To the Drowned Sea,' Marina whispered.

'What did you say?'

'The place where the creature in the nets came from.' That gentle, trusting beautiful face. 'A whole other realm, where there are no dreadnoughts and wars. I'd like to go there one day.'

'There's no such place, Marina.'

'There might be. It's a place that sailors talk about: we have a map at home which my father drew for my mother, and it has the Drowned Sea marked on it.'

Jones gave her a disbelieving look.

'My father did say that it was just a made-up place,' Marina admitted. She frowned. 'Although he'd drawn Pechorin Island on the map as well.'

Jones shrugged. 'I dunno. There do seem to be places in the Far North that not many people know about. That's why Room 40 sent men out to survey the Sea of Murmansk.'

I wish they'd sent me, Marina thought, but didn't say anything for fear of being made fun of. A mere girl could hardly be sent to such inhospitable and remote places.

'It's a shame we can't go ashore here,' she said. 'I'm sad that we've come all this way and I can't even see the town.'

'We don't have time,' Jones said. 'The Commander was quite clear that we can't waste a moment.'

How different Svengejar was from Portsmouth! There were no battleships or large merchant vessels in the small harbour; only small fishing boats were anchored in these peaceful, glassy waters. There were no vast warehouses, no train terminus or grand hotel. The hillside was not draped in rows of stone-built villas. In Svengejar, the painted wooden houses clung to the shoreline, as tightly packed as mussels on a rock. Behind the pitched wooden roofs rose a single church spire as sharp as an icicle. Beyond these buildings, seemingly huddled together for warmth during the coming winter, a low, barren, hill lightly dusted in fresh snow. Beyond that, the vast territories of Muskovy.

Despite the early hour, the town was already stirring. A boat had returned and the night's haul was being unloaded, the nets sagging with the weight of silver-scaled fish. Townsfolk walked briskly along the quay as they went to their work. Horses pulled carts piled with cabbages or timber or milk churns. Two blond-haired children ran along the broad pavement. They wore thick dark jackets, scarves and caps; protection from the bustling wind. They stopped and waved enthusiastically. Marina waved back.

In moments, the *Sea Witch*'s anchor was dropped and the boat was tied up. The engines stopped and, for the first time in days, that constant, throaty noise ceased. A young man from the harbour master's office stood on the quay, waiting to check that the *Sea Witch*'s papers were in order. Commander Denham appeared, wearing his fisherman's duffle coat and woollen hat. He strode purposefully down the gangplank and handed over his documents. The young man scanned them quickly and signalled to a waiting cart, which was filled with coal: the *Sea Witch* would be in port only for as long as it took to take on enough fuel and fresh water to get her up to Pechorin Island and back to Svengejar, and then home.

Brown and Perkins got on with their work, Marina's father returned to the bridge. Jones had signals to wait for. Marina stood with Paddy and watched the Finn-markers go about their business. This was the first time she had ever been to another country, and she was fascinated. Had her mother come from such a place as this? When Marina was younger and had asked her father, he would say things like, 'She came from else-where.' Not much of an answer. But she understood, without his saying, that the question made him sad.

But imagine! Her mother might be living here, or somewhere like it, right now. Marina might, if she looked hard enough, catch sight of her as she walked along the edge of the harbour. For surely her mother would no longer be an invalid, no longer need her canes somewhere where the air was so clean and wholesome – so different from the smog and soot and dust of London. Yes, her mother had come back here just to regain her strength. Made well again, she would walk briskly, her head held high, hoping that one day very soon her beloved daughter would come into the port on a fishing vessel and find her. Oh, her mother would cry and hold Marina tight. Then, wiping away her tears, she would say, 'Come, dear heart. I have a little room made ready for you. There is a pretty bed for you to sleep in and a soft blue rug and the sweetest muslin curtains. You will stay with me and we will never part.'

Of course, the morning being chill, her mother might be wearing a coat over her emerald-green dress, meaning that Marina would have to look very hard to see her. She might appear as mysterious as the cloaked figure Marina noticed walking very quickly along the quay, holding their hood up with pale, slender fingers. But her mother's hair was black, and it was a coil of auburn hair that escaped from the dark prison of the hood. And her mother would never wear red boots that showed an inch of calf.

'Miss Smith?' Marina gasped. What was the secretary to the First Sea Lord doing in Svengejar? Did she have an urgent and secret communiqué to give to a naval commander? But there were no British dreadnoughts in the harbour.

What should Marina do? She didn't have time to go to her father and ask for permission to get off the boat. In the time it would take to explain everything, Miss

Smith would have disappeared. And how could she explain? Marina had, after all, promised to keep their meeting on the train a secret. She looked over at Brown and Perkins: they were busy moving a thick hose towards the fresh-water cistern. There was no one on the bridge.

She ran down the gangplank, expecting someone to call her name. But no call came.

She had escaped.

As Marina scurried along the neat, pretty streets following the cloaked figure, she imagined how Miss Smith's face would light up when she turned to see her. How pleased the young woman would be to hear of Marina's adventures!

'I found my father,' Marina would tell her, 'and I'm a Boy, 2nd class. I get paid sixpence a day, so I have a paid occupation. And I'm so helpful and so useful. I look after the dogs – oh, they are so cute and friendly, even though I mustn't pet them and fuss over them. They talk to me, really. They have such funny, yowly voices, but they really think they can speak.' Miss Smith's smile would be fully dimpled by now. 'And I climbed on to the winch and plucked a Mordavian signals device from the air! I did! And then I fell in the sea, but I didn't let go of it.' (Miss Smith would surely gasp with concern.)

She could even tell Miss Smith that she suspected that there was a spy on the *Sea Witch* – even though it looked like a humble fishing boat, it was really a British navy boat. 'The spy is called Trenchard. He creeps about. He has a scar on his cheek and is surly. I would have sent you a message, but I'm not allowed to use the signals machine.' Although she would have to admit to the impressed Miss Smith that Trenchard didn't have much to spy on.

Through the market square, past the painted wooden church, all the while keeping the cloaked figure in her sight. Miss Smith ran so quickly that it was hard to keep up, and Marina thought she had lost her for a moment, but saw her dart down a narrow side street. Marina caught a blur of white lace at a window as she ran to catch up with the woman.

Miss Smith stood in a doorway, talking earnestly to someone.

Not caring that she was about to interrupt their conversation, Marina raised her hand. 'Miss Smith!'

20

A sharp pain on her shoulder. She was spun round.
'Father!'

'Come with me.' His lips barely moved, his voice was low and quiet. 'Don't speak. Keep walking.'

Her father had glanced over Marina's shoulder, his eyes scanning the street as if he were expecting to see someone. As they walked away, the grip on her shoulder tightened.

She was in dreadful trouble, she could tell. But her father did not say a word, marching her back to the quay and the waiting boat. Brown and Perkins stood on deck, watching anxiously. The moment that they saw the Commander, they must have told the Chief Engineer, as Marina heard the anchor being raised and the engines starting.

A gendarme was watching them as they walked smartly towards their boat. '*Hei!*' he called out. '*Stopp!*'

Marina felt her father's hand loosen slightly on her shoulder. He turned to the gendarme, a pleasant, charming smile on his face. '*God morgen.*'

Marina was surprised: she had no idea that her father could speak another language. She looked up at him. He even looked different without his more usual serious expression. She was about to ask what he'd said, but a squeeze on her shoulder silenced her.

'*Hvor skal dere?*' The gendarme asked, unsmiling.

'*Jeg er på vei til båten min.*'

'*Tar du med ei jente? På båten?*'

Marina's father shrugged. '*Jeg tar sjansen.*' But whatever these words meant, they did not completely satisfy the gendarme.

'*Identitetspapirer?*'

'*På båten. Jeg kan hente dem.*'

The gendarme did not immediately let them go but continued to look them up and down suspiciously. Her father cleared his throat and looked towards the quay. The man grudgingly came to some conclusion in his mind and waved them on.

As they turned to go, Marina asked, 'What did he say?'

Her father didn't reply. Was he still angry with her?

'What did he want? Why did he stop us? We weren't doing anything wrong.'

'*Stans! Engelskmenn!*'

'Keep walking. Look straight ahead.' Her father's pace remained steady. Marina felt the skin on the back of her neck prickle. Was her father in trouble? What could he have done? She heard the shrill note of a whistle pierce the air. And again. The answering sound of boots, running.

They were on the gangplank; her father pushed her up first, pulled the rope off the jetty and threw it up on deck with calm assurance. Behind him, there was confusion on the quay. The young gendarme was gesticulating and pointing at the *Sea Witch*, but no one knew what to do. The *Sea Witch* drew away from the little jetty. The gendarme ran towards the boat, as if he could do something to stop them. He drew out a pistol and aimed it at Brown, who stood, unmoving, on the deck, defiant. Those moments of hesitation and confusion were enough to allow the *Sea Witch* to move out of the harbour and make for the open sea.

*

It was over two hours before her father called for her. Two miserable, wretched hours in the hold, explaining over and over to Paddy and the other dogs why she had got off the boat, even though she had been ordered to stay on board.

'It was a damn fool thing to do, Marina,' he said. 'You had strict orders not to get off the boat and yet, at the moment I am about to leave, you are nowhere to be found. And there you are: strolling through the streets of Svengejar! What on earth possessed you to disobey me?'

As ever, it was hard to reply to him, hard to explain what had gone through her mind in those few seconds when she saw Miss Smith. 'I . . . I thought I saw someone I knew,' she mumbled, looking down at her fingers and knotting them together.

'What?'

'I thought I saw someone I knew, and I just ran after them . . . I didn't think . . . I'm so sorry . . . I was impulsive.'

'Someone you knew? In the most northerly port in Finnmark? What nonsense is this?'

Marina bit her lip. She had promised Miss Smith that she wouldn't tell her father about their meeting, but surely a promise to stranger was less important than answering his questions? She felt awkward. 'It's just that I was looking at the town and I was thinking that it might have been the place where Mama came from . . . And then I saw a woman running along the quay. I thought it might be her.'

Her father's face softened. 'But you know that your mother found it difficult to walk, Marina. Even in the boots I had made for her . . . How could you think it was her?'

'I thought that the air might have made her well again. You said that she had left us because she was very ill.'

Her father sighed. 'There's no air on this earth that could have made your mother well, Marina. She was very sick.'

'Which was why she had to leave us. Ivy said Mama couldn't breathe in the dirty London air.'

'For once, Ivy is right.'

'But where did Mama go?'

Her father's face looked drawn and pale. 'She went home,' he whispered. 'Where she thought she would be safe.'

'But where is ho—'

'Sir?' Jones stood in the doorway.

'Yes?'

'Just got a message from Room 40, sir.'

'And?'

'There's been another British fishing vessel . . .'

'Yes?'

'Disappeared, sir. She's . . . She's . . . missing.'

'Details?'

'The *Maggie* – a trawler out of Dundee – was last heard from at 0800 hours, GMT.'

'Where was she?'

'Latitude 72 degrees north, and longitude 33 degrees east.'

'The Sea of Murmansk,' the Commander said, quietly. 'What was she doing that far north?'

'She had tried to turn back, sir. But she was being pursued, sir, by a Mordavian battleship.'

'Like all the others,' the Commander muttered.

'Thing is, once the *Maggie* entered the Sea of Murmansk, the Mordavians didn't follow her. She disappeared an hour later.'

'We're sure of that?'

'No one can get any signal from the boat.'

'No signal at all?'

'She didn't even send an SOS, sir. She just sent . . . well, it wasn't even much of a message, sir. Room 40 sounded quite agitated.'

'What do you mean?'

'The skipper of the *Maggie* said that he was taking his men to . . .'

'Yes?'

'The place didn't make any sense, sir. All Room 40 said was that it wasn't marked on any map.'

Finchin now appeared. 'Commander. We might have a bit of trouble, sir.'

'I know. Another British boat has gone missing.'

'I think this might be a different sort of trouble, sir.'

'What do you mean?'

'It would seem, sir, that we are being chased.'

21

Marina counted three battleships on the horizon. There was no mistaking the pointed prows, gun turrets and powerful engines of the Mordavian Annihilator Class dreadnought.

Her father had given the Chief Engineer instructions to push the engines to their limit and take the *Sea Witch*'s speed up to twenty-five knots. This should mean that they could outrun the heavier boats, which would not be able to travel at much more than twenty-one knots, but it would take a few hours.

But the battleships were not left behind. Over the next hour, they gained on the *Sea Witch*.

Brown and Perkins stood on the stern of the boat to get a good look at their pursuers. Marina sidled up to them to listen.

'They're coming for us,' Perkins said. 'Though what they want with us is anyone's guess. We're not doing anything wrong. What's got into them, chasing a fishing boat?'

'Beats me,' Brown replied. 'But they don't need to have any reason, with gun turrets that size.' Neither man seemed particularly bothered by the prospect of being chased down by enemy boats. 'Look at them, though, Perkins. I don't think I've ever seen such beauties. That's the new Annihilator Class, every one of them built in the last year.'

'What you reckon about them guns?' Perkins asked him. 'They don't look as big as what's on our warships.'

'Aye, they don't look as useful as ours, but they can fire 'em quicker,' Brown said, thoughtfully. 'The boats are lighter, too. The steel hull is not as thick. It makes them faster in the water and easier to turn.'

'Aren't you scared?' Marina asked.

'Not much point being scared,' Brown said, shrugging. 'Either we'll get away from them or we won't. There's not much an Able Seaman can do about it. It's up to the Chief Engineer and that engine of his.' He pulled out a small pipe and started packing it with tobacco. 'We might as well go the mess, Perkins. Play cards. I'll get Trenchard to keep a look out. He likes being on deck. You need to get inside as well,' he said to Marina.

'But isn't there anything else we can do?' It seemed cowardly, somehow, to go inside and play cards.

'We're being pursued by Mordavian dreadnoughts, Perkins. The Boy, here, wants to know if there's anything else we can do.'

Perkins frowned for a second. 'No.'

The warships kept the *Sea Witch* just within firing distance. The day after their appearance, a freezing sea fog fell. But the boats could still be identified by the soft glow of their red fog lights – like monsters' eyes, Marina thought.

Marina asked Jones why he did not signal for help.

'Any British warship coming to our aid would make it seem the British are up for a fight,' he explained. 'The Admiralty won't take the risk. We're on our own.'

The fog lifted. The *Sea Witch* continued north. She had no choice; there was no turning back. The mood of the crew was subdued, but they went about their tasks and tried to keep the ominous presence of the powerful dreadnoughts out of their thoughts.

Marina felt that she couldn't breathe. 'It's like we're in a net,' she told Paddy. He put his head back and told her he agreed. She thought about that strange creature she had put back in the sea; to her, being trapped was the worst sort of unhappiness, a living death.

'They think they're so invincible,' Marina said to herself as she looked at the narrow grey prows slicing through the water like knives. But what were those high-sided grey hulls in comparison to the sea? Guns wouldn't help them if the sea rose up. Those boats would be helpless, because the power of a rising wave was unstoppable. How would those dreadnoughts cope with waves the size of mountains?

These thoughts gave Marina an odd feeling. She no longer felt she was on a boat in the middle of a cold, northern sea. Nor was she part of the sea that moved around her. If she closed her eyes and took a breath, she felt that she *was* the sea. There was no telling where she ended and the sea began. And as she became the sea, she could feel the currents, the tides, the movement of the waves, all as one powerful dance within her. Another wave moved away from her, so high that it blocked out the dreadnoughts, higher and more solid than any steel hull. And the wind – she could feel the wind stirring in answer to the waves . . . And the clouds came chasing towards her, a shadow sea in the sky, black and swollen with freezing rain that would fall heavy and sharp as nails. She could breathe in and feel a wave rising from the very depths of the ocean. The further it had to climb, the more powerful it would be. And then she realized that it was her breath that was moving these waves. She could summon one from the depths by breathing in, making it rise up and up in front of her. She could hold her breath, with that majestic mountain of black water in front of her, and then, breathing out, she could send it racing towards those wretched Mordavian warships – which looked as terrifying now as a child's toy on a boating lake . . .

'Marina! Inside!' Her father, dragging her away from the prow. 'It's a storm!'

Surprised, she saw now how the waves lashed the deck of the boat, how the rain hurled itself from the clouds, puncturing the surface of the sea. The wind took her breath away. She was no longer the sea, she was just a small, fragile twelve-year-old at the mercy of a sudden, violent gale. Her father put his arm around her and they struggled towards the mess.

All the crew were gathered there, apart from the Chief

Engineer and his Mate, whose job it was to somehow keep the *Sea Witch*'s engine moving in the hope they could outrun the storm.

'Why did I get no warning of this?' Commander Denham wiped the rain from his face.

'There was no warning, sir,' Jones answered, his face pale and his hair plastered to his head. Even the short step from the Signals Room to the mess had drenched him. 'The forecast was for minimal swell and good visibility.'

'Well, the storm's here now,' Brown said. He held a metal bowl close to his chest – even the most able of seamen could get sick in a storm.

Perkins muttered something under his breath.

'Cut yer wittering on,' Brown groaned. 'I can do without your nonsense.'

'But don't you see?' Perkins stared out at the rain battering the porthole and the mountainous waves that threatened to topple on to the boat. 'This storm came from nowhere. Nowhere! I tell you, it's a witch storm. It's been whistled up to drown us all!'

'I'll whistle up my fists if you don't shut it,' Brown mumbled.

'That's enough,' Commander Denham ordered. 'There's no need for such foolishness. When we face these dangers, we behave like sailors, like navy men. There's no room for superstition on this boat. We will proceed as we would in any difficult situation. All men present? Call out your names.'

The men gave their names in order of rank.

The wind screamed and the waves rose higher. The *Sea Witch* was spun round, upended, tossed about like a ball. And then the engines went silent. With no power, the boat would have no chance of outrunning the storm.

'The dogs. My dogs!' Marina tried to struggle free. 'They'll be so frightened.'

Trenchard, who had been staring morosely into nothingness, lumbered to his feet. He was almost flung against the wall for his trouble. 'The dogs have had it. And so have we. Unless I can get down to the engine room to help the Engineer. If we can't get the engines started ...'

Before anyone could stop him, Trenchard lunged for the door. 'I'd rather be swept off deck trying to do something useful than sit here like a sardine in a tin!'

Seconds later, the door blew open again to reveal Trenchard, battling to stay upright as a torrent of water rushed over the deck. A wave reared up and swept across him. He was knocked sideways, his arm twisted at a ghastly angle, although he managed to keep himself from the clutches of the sea.

The *Sea Witch* climbed the side of another wave. Trenchard, drenched and clutching his twisted arm, launched himself across the deck. Another wave teetered above him, like a vast tower about to fall. And then it crashed down on top of him.

The next wave rose, and, terrifying, a black shape rose within it – some ancient, murderous sea creature which had risen from the depths, drawn by the taste for a mortal's flesh.

The door swung shut. Marina sobbed, burying her face in her father's thick sweater. 'It's my fault. I did this. I didn't mean to. I didn't mean to.' She had summoned those waves, but had not thought how she could stop them.

He stroked her hair. 'Not your fault, not your fault,' he repeated. His chest rose and fell, like a wave on a calm sea, and the movement comforted her. 'No man is a match for the sea . . .'

The boat tipped to one side and the men groaned in unison. Jones's lips moved soundlessly, perhaps in some sort of prayer. But Marina, her body lurching from side to side, felt peaceful; there was no need to cry out.

'You can have me,' she whispered to the sea. 'I won't fight.'

22

Hours later, shivering with cold, their nerves shredded, the crew of the *Sea Witch* stumbled out of the mess and on to the deck. After the screaming symphony of the storm, the silence that greeted them was eerie, as if the world had been washed clean of sound. The waves, which hours before had been as tall and impenetrable as mountains, had disappeared: the sea was flat and black, like polished basalt. The sky had changed too: the Arctic days were being cut short by the sun which would no longer rise above the horizon. The Arctic night would be a winter long.

There were no Mordavian boats on the horizon: they had fallen back, been blown off course, or been submerged in the violent storm. The *Sea Witch* sailed on alone, into the Sea of Murmansk, where six British boats had already disappeared.

And yet Marina's pulse jumped with the joy of being alive. She took a deep breath of air: cold, sharp and clear. It was like breathing water from the deepest part of the sea. How foolish to think that she had caused that storm. Now, as the boat glided through flat, black water, she knew that the sea would hardly do her bidding. She was a twelve-year-old girl, not a conjuror of storms.

Her breath turned to mist. She glanced at Jones. He looked thin and pale, his black hair standing up and his clothes wet and dishevelled.

The Commander's face was grey and drawn as he spoke. 'One of our crew has given his life to the sea. We stand together now to remember him and hope that he is at peace.'

Brown wiped a tear from his eye. He looked embarrassed when he saw Marina notice. 'I didn't like Trenchard, it's true, but no one deserves to die like that. Years and years at sea, and I'm no less afeared of a death by drowning.'

Marina asked Brown to help her open the door to the hold. The dogs had been quiet all this time and she feared the worst. But as they heard the bolts being pulled back, they set up their welcome chorus. Marina climbed down, calling each one by name. They stood up and called their names back to her. But there was one who still lay on his side. Paddy. Marina was so keen to open the cage that her fingers made a muddle of the job. The dogs jumped up and stuck their paws through the bars, making the job harder, but eventually the padlock obeyed her hands, the door swung open and the dogs spilled out. She crawled in to be next to Paddy. Still he didn't move, didn't thump his tail on the straw. She put her hand into his deep fur, her fingers disappearing. She felt his nose. It was warm. He had been sick.

'Paddy,' she breathed. 'Oh, Paddy, what's wrong?' Hearing her voice, his eyes flickered and he gave a great shuddering sigh.

She sat with him for a while. The *Sea Witch* drifted. The engine had been damaged in the storm and she could hear the Chief Engineer banging about in the engine room. Above, the men were checking the damage to the boat. The rope was missing from the winch, but they had no need for nets and fishing for now.

She went to fetch Paddy some fresh water. As she

was filling the bucket, Perkins sidled up to her.

'Was it you?' he said quietly, keeping an eye on the Commander and Finchin.

'What do you mean?'

'I saw you. On the stern. When the storm came. You wasn't afeared. I've just heard that those with your blood – don't take offence, I mean nothing by it – but those with your blood, they can call up a storm.'

'What do you mean, my blood?'

Perkins looked troubled. 'Nothing, miss. I meant nothing.'

A cry of alarm. 'Ice!' It was Brown, shouting; and again, his voice hoarse, 'Iiiiiiiiiice!'

'Jones! Denham!' her father barked.

Marina scrabbled out of the cage and hurried to answer her father. 'Commander!'

She saw Brown hanging over the edge of the boat, his eyes fixed on the horizon. There, a huge castle of ice floated towards them.

'Keep looking for icebergs,' her father ordered. 'Get Cook and his Mate out here, too. Perkins, take soundings. The sea will be getting shallower. I don't want the hull ripped open by ice. And Brown, get the Chief Engineer to give us more power, so that we don't drift towards those things. They're more dangerous than a

Mordavian destroyer. Quieter, too. Finchin, steady at the wheel. We're still heading north, but be prepared to swing the boat to starboard.'

Could her father not feel the current, Marina wondered. Some channel of water deep beneath the hull of the *Sea Witch* was pulling them on. They would skirt the iceberg, just. She knew the current would not fail them. The boat was being pulled north, like a child's toy on a piece of string. But how could she explain?

The vast white ice castle creaked in agony as it floated through the flat black water. The engine found more strength and the boat moved more swiftly away from its deadly progress.

Marina was about to return to nurse Paddy when she saw something else on the horizon. 'Ice!' she cried out. 'Portside!'

'And starboard!' Jones yelled.

A whole range of ice. Her father leapt down the steps from the bridge and joined them on deck. 'At last – Pechorin Island.' His eyes glittered with excitement as he turned to take in the ice cliffs that seemed to have risen up from the sea without warning.

'Finchin? Hold her steady until I give you the command. Don't turn too soon.'

The little boat sailed round the edge of this ice

fortress. And, like a fortress, it seemed just as impossible to enter.

'Now!' her father cried. 'Portside! And be quick about it!'

The prow of the *Sea Witch* turned sharply, as if attempting to throw herself at the ice. But a narrow gap had appeared in the ice wall and a black path of sea-water led them into the frozen interior of the island.

'Easy! Easy!' her father called out.

The engine stuttered as the boat was held in the water against the current. And then, painfully slowly, the *Sea Witch* nosed through a narrow corridor in the ice. The channel was so narrow that Marina and Jones could have put their hands out and touched the glistening blue-white battlements. Outcrops of ice hung over the deck. The winch arm caught on one of these and a huge block of ice fell into the water.

The *Sea Witch* now inched slowly into an inlet. Ahead, a natural harbour, where she could drop her anchor, and above, skeletal grey cliffs broke through a glistening white mantle of snow.

Looking into the clear water, Marina could see soft mounds of ice moulded by the current. It was as if she could look through a mirror to the world behind and beyond the reflected image.

A spit of ice jutted out into the black water: the *Sea Witch* came alongside, the Commander himself taking the wheel for such a delicate manoeuvre. The gangplank was dropped and within moments her father appeared already changed into his Arctic gear. He ran down on to the ice. 'Hurry!' he shouted. 'Get the equipment unloaded!'

Brown handed Marina a pile of woollen clothes: so many extra sweaters and hats and gloves that, once she had dressed, she could hardly move.

Her father paced up and down as he waited, impatiently.

The Commander would be travelling light: one crate, a tent, and supplies for the forty-eight hours he would be away mending the faulty sonar transmitter.

Marina went down into the hold to bring up the dogs. They were ecstatic, as if they could smell snow and sense the land over which they were eager to run. But Paddy was still sick. He whimpered as he saw the dogs being taken up, but there was nothing that could be done.

'I'll be back,' Marina told him. 'I won't leave you alone for long.'

On land after so many days at sea, the dogs barked and ran around, cocking their legs against the ridges of snow and leaving yellow-stained holes.

Brown strapped a kitbag, heavy with tools, to the top of the sledge. 'You've done a good job with those dogs,' he said approvingly. 'Shame Paddy won't be joining them.'

'He's too sick.' Marina sniffed. 'I don't know what's wrong with him.'

'Best to leave him quiet,' Brown told her. 'He'll pull through. He's a strong 'un.'

Her father tramped towards the sledge. He was wearing a full-length fur coat and his fur mittens. He had the same preoccupied air as he had had on the last day in London: eager to be off.

Finchin followed him on to the ice to wish him well. Marina bent down and slyly kissed each dog on the top of his head and told him to behave and do exactly as the Commander ordered.

'I'll see you all very soon,' she whispered into ears and fur. 'Remember that I've looked after you well, and given you plenty to eat, and I'm not really sad that you're going. Well, perhaps just a bit . . . but you mustn't be unhappy or feel tired, because you must bring my father back safely. He has important work to do! He's mending a broken transmitter. I know it doesn't sound very important, but you must still do your best.' The dogs barked as if they understood.

The Commander and Finchin shook hands. Her father stepped on to the running board of the sledge. 'Farewell, Finchin.' he said. 'I'll see you in two days.'

'Does that give you enough time to get to the whaling station, sir?'

'It does. And even if it doesn't, the *Sea Witch* must sail on Thursday at 1100 hours, sharp.'

'I can wait longer, sir.'

'No need. I'll be back in good time.'

Finchin nodded. 'Farewell, sir,' he said, as if the Commander were doing nothing more than going for a stroll on a summer's afternoon.

Marina couldn't stop herself. She put her arms round her father. It felt like hugging a bear. 'Please. Be very careful.'

Her father gently took her arms away from him. 'What's all this?'

Marina felt embarrassed in front of Finchin. 'I . . . I don't know. I just want you to be careful. This is such a strange place. And you'll be all alone.'

'I've got all the company I need, Marina,' her father said, looking at the dogs. 'No tears, now. They'll freeze on your skin. Like pearls.' He wiped her cheek with his fur glove.

'Take care, sir,' Finchin said, his voice suddenly

serious. 'I know you're the only man for the job. It's good work you're doing.'

'Hiiiiiiii,' Commander Denham called, and the dogs leapt forward with such eagerness that he had to right himself. The runners made a shussssing noise on the snow. Marina ran alongside for as long as her lungs and her legs would let her. But the dogs, eager to run, easily pulled ahead. Her father called out again, raising his arm in a salute, although he didn't turn back.

His face was set to the north.

23

Marina kept her eyes on the dark figure as it moved away from her. The dogs ran furiously and within minutes her father was just a blurred smudge. She strained her eyes, hoping to keep him close to her by the power of her gaze alone. But when she next blinked, he was gone.

'Do you mind if I stay on land for a while?' Marina asked as they tramped back to the boat.

'Just don't stay out too long,' Finchin said. 'It's bitter cold, and your father won't thank me if he's kept you safe only for you to be frozen to death.'

Marina waited until Finchin had climbed back on to

the *Sea Witch* and then, not caring about the cold, lay down on the snow.

The stars trembled above her, so close she felt she could reach out and touch one. Just forty-eight hours and they would leave this island made of twilight, ice and air. 'I could never have believed such a place existed,' she said, drawing lines between the stars with her finger. Pechorin Island. Her father had drawn a map of this place for her mother. Had she dreamt of coming to such a distant, lost realm? Even though she was a cripple and could scarcely cross a room unaided? Perhaps here her lungs would drink the ice-cold air and her legs would become strong as she ran across the snow.

Jones's face hung above her. 'I thought I'd find you out here.' He sat down next to her. 'Don't be sad. The Commander won't be long,' he said.

'I wish he hadn't gone.'

'He has his orders, Marina.'

'Oh, you and your stupid orders. You'll do anything if it's an order. Would you jump off the ship if I gave you the order?'

'If you were my commanding officer, I'd have to.'

Marina sighed. 'It's all so stupid.' She felt cross and out of sorts.

Jones picked up some snow and made a snowball. He threw it towards the water. 'Your father will return soon, and then we can head back to Portsmouth.'

'I'm not sure I want to go . . .' she said. 'I'll get sent away to that wretched school.'

'I'd do anything to be sent to school,' Jones said quietly.

'What are you talking about?' She sat up, a bonnet of snow on her dark hair.

'I'd like to learn all sorts of things,' he muttered, looking embarrassed. 'If I went to school, I could even be a university man. Like your father. Then I could work in Room 40.' He sighed. 'It will never happen, of course. My family don't have the money. They need me to work. Need me to earn.' He shifted uncomfortably. 'I mean, I'm proud to help them, I really am. Bryn – he's the littlest – is getting new boots. He couldn't use the ones we all had because they're worn out.'

Now Marina felt ashamed. Of course. There would have been no money for this boy's education. It wasn't just girls who had very little say in what their life might be. Boys from families such as Jones's could not hope for a life of their own choosing. Their lives had already been chosen by those in charge – the pit- or mill-owners who owned the towns and villages their workers lived in.

'Do you think we've disappeared?' she asked him. 'Like those other fishing vessels? It feels like we've fallen through the bottom of the ocean to some other world.' A world between dreaming and waking, she thought. Between the dark and the light, between the world she knew and some other, forgotten realm.

On board, Brown had brought out his accordion, and his sad song about a boat being sung to the bottom of the sea drifted across to them.

'It's a strange place,' Jones said. 'I could never have imagined anywhere like this. It feels like the place you'd come to after you've died.' He blew his breath out in a cloud. 'I can't shake the sadness. Do you feel it? It's like a sea mist that's fallen around me.'

'Perhaps you just miss your family.'

'Perhaps.' Jones was quiet for a moment and then asked, 'Where do you think your mam is?'

'I don't know.' But Marina wanted to think that her mother was in a place like this. It seemed like an enchanted realm of deep magic and possibility, where silence, at last, might sing.

Restless and unable to sleep, Marina found herself outside the door to her father's cabin. She wrinkled her nose as she caught the faint acrid scent of his tobacco.

Where was he now?

She tried the door; it swung open. That was odd, because her father was normally so against leaving his doors unlocked.

She went inside and sat down on her father's narrow bed. It was as if no one had ever slept there, so entirely had his presence been removed.

She patted the bed and Paddy jumped up to sit next to her. She reached for her father's pillow and hugged it close to her body.

Something hard dug into her chest. She reached into the pillowcase and pulled out a notebook. She was going to put it back, but, holding it in her hands, tracing his initials stamped in gold on the cover, she thought she might just look at the first page.

She felt bad as she opened it, as if she were stealing something, but that didn't stop her. She remembered how she had crept into her mother's room when her father had returned from some voyage at sea. She couldn't have been more than seven, and her mother's locked room exerted an influence over her that she couldn't shake off. Ivy had completed her weekly dusting and airing and had left the room unlocked. Marina had slipped in and run her fingers over the cut-glass scent bottles on her mother's dressing table. One still had a dark liquid inside. The bottle was heavy and Marina's fingers were clumsy. The bottle had slipped through her hands and smashed on the floor. The scent that surrounded her – dark, mysterious and heavy as water – almost paralysed her. It was only her father's heavy footsteps on the stairs that shook her out of herself and forced her to hide behind a chair. Her father ran into the room. 'Annabel?' he called, his face alight, expectant. But when he saw the bottle, he shouted to Ivy to come and clear up, and retired to his study, slamming the door.

Marina settled herself on the bed and took a deep breath. She thought that she could, even now, still smell her mother's mysterious perfume on the pages of the notebook.

The opening pages were as she might have expected: handwritten charts of Pechorin Island and lists of co-ordinates of the sort used to plan a sea voyage covered the paper in her father's neat, square handwriting.

But the next few pages were held together by a rusty paper clip. She pulled it off and the leaves sprang apart.

Her father could draw, she knew that. When he spent months at sea, his letters home to her were always decorated with an exquisite line drawing of a three-masted ship, which appeared to sail on the waves of his handwriting below. But the drawings Marina was looking at now were quite different. The small pages were almost entirely covered with ink drawings of sea creatures, all in exquisite detail. There were starfish and whales and seals – those she could recognize. But there was another, troubling hybrid creature. It had an arrestingly beautiful face and hair that trailed like seaweed, but the limbs that coiled around her father's writing were the limbs of an octopus.

Marina closed the notebook and slipped it back into the pillowcase.

Perhaps her father was unhinged. That was the word Ivy used about people whose minds were sick. 'They look the same as you and me,' she would say. 'But inside their heads –' and she'd tap her temple and mouth – 'broken.'

Marina put her arms round Paddy's neck and tried to summon up everything she could remember of the days after her mother's disappearance. No one had told her where her mother had gone. Her father retired to his study and did not even come out for meals; Ivy had to leave food on a tray outside the door and take it away later, untouched. But some time not long after – Marina was still wearing black mourning ribbons in her hair – her father took her from her dolls and dressed her in her best coat and bonnet and they went in a hansom cab to London Bridge. He held her hand too tight as he pulled her along to the very centre of the bridge. She whined and cried and wanted to go home. But her father ignored her. And then he lifted her up and held her on the parapet of the bridge. She could scarcely make out the waves below, but she could hear the slap of the water and the lazy chug of the barges as they passed beneath. She was sobbing properly now, but her father took no notice. 'Here she is!' he cried out into the fog. 'Will you come and take her?' Marina had begged him to let her down. And then, so gently, he had lifted her down and held her to his chest and promised her that he would take care of her.

Years later, she found her father's behaviour was no less puzzling. He had risked his life, and that of his crew, to sail north to repair a sonar transmitter somewhere on a deserted island.

Like the sea at its deepest, her father was unfathomable.

24

The next day, Paddy was much better: his nose was cold and his eyes were bright. Marina fashioned him a sledge from a packing crate which had contained some of her father's equipment. Then she made him a harness out of rope. She took him on to the ice and let him pull her along, the pair of them enjoying the quivering air.

The mood on the *Sea Witch* had worsened overnight. Brown and Perkins were bickering. 'Why did we come back?' Perkins hissed.

'Because we do as we're told.'

'But I told you when we left here last time, I'd never

come back.'

'Keep your trap shut. You do yourself no good letting your thoughts wander.'

Jones looked feverish, his colour high and his hair damp with sweat, despite the freezing air. Cook shouted at his Mate and the potatoes were burned. At dinner, Finchin arrived late, which was shocking because he was always entirely punctual. He looked as if he hadn't slept for days. His clothes were dishevelled and he mumbled only a few words before they ate.

A plate smashed. 'What the—' Brown exclaimed.

Perkins stared out of the porthole at the silent water, unbothered by the broken china at his feet.

'Get yourself together, man!' Finchin's voice crackled.

But Perkins took no notice. He stood up, swaying slightly. Sweat broke out on his brow. 'Can't you hear it?' he whispered.

'Hear what?' Brown muttered. 'I can't hear nothing but Cook with his pots and pans.'

'That voice.'

'There's no voice, man!' Finchin snapped.

'I tell you there is! It's calling to me!' And with that, Perkins leapt towards the door of the mess and ran out. Stunned, the others heard his boots thudding on the deck.

Seconds later, a cry of anguish and a splash.

Finchin now shook himself, as if waking up. Brown was already out of the door. Marina and Jones followed them. On deck, Marina watched as Brown unhooked the lifesaver – why could so few sailors actually swim? – and threw it over the side.

Finchin, his face creased with anxiety, looked at Perkins bobbing about in the sea. 'He'll not last more than a few minutes in that water.' He clenched his fists. 'Damned stupid man.'

Brown now had a boat hook and was leaning over the side. 'Just hold on to it!' he cried. 'We'll do the work for you.' But Perkins thrashed about, laughing. He wouldn't reach for it – he seemed determined to perish.

They threw him a rope. Perkins yelled at them to leave him, but Brown managed to drop the net over him. Seconds later, Perkins was hauled on to the deck.

'Get him inside,' Finchin snapped. 'And keep him there.'

Perkins was strangely quiet now. He didn't shout or fling his arms around or attempt to throw himself in the sea. Brown led him away.

Finchin looked suddenly careworn. 'It will be good to get away from this place,' he muttered. Paddy yowled in agreement.

But Marina felt differently. Pechorin Island was barren, uninhabited; there was nothing to see. So why did she feel this urgent tugging in her chest to go north?

She woke early the next morning. Her father would be returning that day, although time seemed to run differently on this island of twilight. She sprang out of her hammock and rushed towards the galley.

'Do you have any of that foul stuff you made for my father?'

'Pemmican?' The cook reached for a tin bowl filled with a strange mess of grease, dried meat and currants. This was what her father had taken with him to feed himself and the dogs on their arduous journey across the snow.

'The minute I see Father, I'm going to take this and give the dogs a treat,' she explained. 'For bringing him home safely.'

Cook took a lump and formed it into a large ball, like a Christmas pudding, and wrapped it in a calico square. 'It won't be long now,' he said, looking more anxious than Marina would have liked. 'And we'll all be glad when we're heading back to Portsmouth.'

Marina didn't wait to eat breakfast but went straight up on deck. She unwrapped the pemmican and stuck her finger into the grease and put it on her tongue. 'Urgh.' Poor father. How he would enjoy his first meal back on the *Sea Witch*.

'What time is it?' she asked Brown.

He looked troubled. 'Time to leave this blasted place.'

'Any sign of him?' Finchin joined her on deck. He had brought her a tin mug of tea and he stood and drank his own, the steam rising in front of his face. Nothing showed that Finchin was tense or in any way worried that her father would not arrive in time. But he kept checking his watch; like her father, he wore one of the new style of watch that was attached to his wrist with two leather straps. 'It shouldn't be long, now,' he muttered.

But still there was no small dark figure on the horizon, no voice urging the dogs on. Finchin went up to the bridge, where he gave the order for the *Sea Witch*'s engines to be started. When he returned, he came with binoculars. He scanned the horizon. He checked his watch again.

'The minute I see Father, I want to set off to see him. I've got pemmican for the dogs – to give them a treat and make them run this last bit faster. They'll be exhausted, you see,' Marina told him. 'I'll go on to the ice.'

'No,' Finchin said, quietly but firmly. 'You'll wait on the boat.'

Brown was on deck, waiting for the order to bring up the anchor. Perkins started yelling from the confines of his cabin. 'Let me out! Let me out! I need to get there! I can hear her calling for me!'

Jones came out of the Signals Room, his collar up and his cap pulled down, shivering in the cold.

'He's coming,' Marina said.

'Where?' Finchin lifted his binoculars again.

'I just know that he is,' Marina said, her jaw tense.

'Brown! Anchor.'

'But you can't,' Marina gasped. 'You just can't. Brown! Leave the anchor. He's coming, don't you see? My father is coming.'

'I could have waited,' Finchin said quietly, 'if we had seen him in the distance. But I have orders to leave on the hour, Marina.'

'I don't care about your stupid orders. You can't leave him here!'

She saw Jones move towards her, unsure of himself, but knowing that he should say something.

'Brown!' Finchin snapped. 'Anchor! And that's an order! Or do you want to be court-marshalled when we get back to port?'

Marina heard that grinding clank of the anchor being raised. 'But *please*, sir!' She pulled on Finchin's arm. 'Just a few more minutes.'

Finchin's face did not change, but he did not give the order to raise the gangplank.

'Aye, we've got a few more minutes yet,' Brown told her as he joined them at the rail, desperately searching the horizon. 'Keep your eyes peeled. We'll be off the minute he's on board.'

Paddy jumped up and put two paws on the side of the boat. His ears were pricked. Could he hear the dogs? Could he hear the sound of her father's sledge on the snow? He put his head back and yowled.

'Quiet,' Marina whispered, patting his side. She narrowed her eyes to focus on the horizon. But Paddy would not be quiet. He yowled and barked.

And then, as if answering some call that only he could hear, he ran down the gangplank and set off across the ice.

'Leave him!' Finchin put his hand on Marina's shoulder. 'Brown? Get that gangplank raised.'

'But we can't leave Paddy!' Marina shook herself free. 'And we can't leave my father.' She threw down her mug, picked up her sledge and half ran, half slid down the gangplank and on to the ice.

'Hey!' Brown shouted after her. 'What are you doing? Come back!'

'We need to stop her!' Finchin roared. 'Brown! Jones! Follow me!'

Marina heard their boots on the gangplank and their feet crunching on the ice behind her. But she kept after Paddy.

'Wait, you rascal,' she called. And the dog did stop. She caught up with him and slipped the harness over his shoulders, expecting any second to feel Finchin's hand on her shoulder. 'Go!' she cried, leaping on to the sledge.

But the men kept after her; they wouldn't give up. Jones called out to her. She couldn't listen. Paddy was right to have run away. She couldn't go back to the *Sea Witch* with her father missing in this barren land.

When she next looked round, she saw that Brown had given up the chase. He was bending over as if he were winded. Then Jones stopped. He looked like he had a stitch. Finchin kept running for the longest, but even he couldn't catch an animal bred to run for eighteen hours a day.

Ahead lay the strange landscape of Pechorin Island. Endless snow, pleated by the wind. Rocky outcrops nudging up through thick white blankets like waking skeletons.

How long had they run for? She stopped for a moment and adjusted the scarf she had pulled up over her mouth. Paddy's breathing eased. She dug in her pocket and brought out the pemmican. She broke off a chunk and held it out for him. He chewed and swallowed and looked up at her for more. 'We're going to have to ration ourselves, Paddy,' she told him. 'This is all I've got.' Her father's words floated back to her. *A journey is all about planning, Marina. Much more time should be taken in the planning than in the journey itself. That way you will always come back safe.*

She had taken no time to plan, but she had had no choice. She could not leave her father on this island. She shook her head to dislodge the image of herself blundering about in the snow. She must not let such thoughts get the better of her. The map of this island in her father's notebook had clearly shown a dotted line to the north and the whaling station. She could see the North Star ahead of her. As long as she followed that, she surely could not go wrong.

Marina felt comforted seeing Paddy, fortified by food. She shouldn't have fed him – he would run better on an empty stomach, but he had been so poorly, she reasoned, that she couldn't resist. He strained at the harness. He was a good companion to have in this permanent dusk.

She concentrated on keeping moving for the next couple of hours or so (it was hard to tell how long they had been travelling in this trembling half-light). The wind had picked up, and it was coming from the north. She half skated along on the sledge to save Paddy's strength. Her eyes streamed and she felt her tears turn to ice. Paddy started panting heavily. He still had not regained his strength. She had no idea how long they had been travelling for but watching his laboured breathing, she knew she would need to rest him.

Marina jumped off the sledge and undid Paddy's harness. He relieved himself and then looked up at her, expectant. She mustn't give him any more food. She pulled the lump of pemmican out of her pocket. Had she really given him such a large piece last time? She took a small lump and put it on her tongue. Cook was right; it did taste better in the cold with no hope of any other food. She licked the grease off her hand. She wanted more, but she must make the pemmican last. She shook herself. She mustn't allow herself to feel tired and hungry. She must keep travelling. But clouds now covered the sky and she could not be sure of her direction.

She realized too, now that they had stopped, that she was bone-tired. She took one last bite of pemmican and then quickly wrapped it back up in the calico square and stuffed it back in her pocket. She dropped down on her haunches. The snow danced in flurries. She closed her eyes for a second. 'I won't sleep,' she told herself. 'I'll just rest my eyes from the wind. I'm not sleeping. It's just a short rest. I must find Father. So I'm not sleeping. Sleep . . . Mustn't . . .'

Marina licked her lips. She tasted meringues and marshmallows. She should sing to keep herself awake. There was that song which Brown sang on the *Sea Witch*. It was very sad, but she couldn't think of anything else. How did it go?

'As I sailed out one day, one day,' she half-sang, half-whispered.

'And being not far from land,

I spied a mermaid sitting on a rock,

with a comb and a glass in her hand.'

25

The wind dropped and the clouds lifted. The stars, hard and bright, illuminated the snow. Marina distracted herself by imagining the look of joy on her father's face when she found him. It was better than thinking about this trembling wilderness where spirits surely roamed – she glimpsed them out of the corner of her eye, but if she turned her head, they would disappear.

Marina and Paddy went on, but they hardly seemed to make any progress. Marina got off the sledge and walked alongside the dog. Paddy's breathing was ragged and he whimpered. With a sour taste in her mouth,

Marina realized that it wasn't just that he hadn't fully recovered from his sickness; her brave, funny Paddy was frightened. And his fear infected her. They were being stalked by spirits who lived under the snow, who wanted to warm themselves by drinking their hot, fresh blood. Once she had that thought in her mind, she couldn't shake it. Her pulse quickened, she thought she would go mad with fear. Paddy howled his distress, kept looking to one side, as if he could see the dark shadow of the spirit that stalked them.

She could hear it, too.

It was under the snow. It was large. It was black. It cut through the dark sea under the ice with the grace and ease of a spear through the air. It was horrifying – and it was making straight for them. The spirit groaned in pleasure that it would soon have such tasty blood-filled morsels in its jaws. Marina tried to run, but Paddy was on his last legs, staggering along: only his fear kept him from falling.

The black shadow slid up to them. She was trans-fixed. How much longer did they have before they were snatched? She saw the ridge of ice too late. A sharp judder. She lurched to the side, then tipped backwards. A dull thud as she hit the ground.

Marina let go of Paddy's harness. 'Just go,' she

whispered, but Paddy would not move. 'Just go, you stupid dog. Save yourself.'

She tasted blood. She had bitten her cheek as she fell. Her head was too heavy to move. Fear flowed through her veins. The spirit slid forward, pushing the ice apart. It rose up, blacker than night. There was a horrifying grinding and clanking noise as the jaws opened.

'I'm sorry, Paddy.' Marina now grabbed the dog and buried her face in his thick fur. She closed her eyes, held her breath. 'Please let this be quick.'

'We've got her!' A woman's voice, triumphant.

Marina opened her eyes and tried to lift herself up from the snow. She saw an extraordinary vision walking towards her. The figure wore a white fur coat, cut short to show off dainty white laced boots, the fur lining peeping over the cuff. A white-gloved hand pushed submariner's goggles up on to a pile of auburn hair.

So this was the snow spirit who had come to take her.

The First Sea Lord's secretary, Miss Gaby Smith.

Marina was pulled up gently from the snow. A soft fur pelt was wrapped around her shoulders. And all the while, Miss Smith looked at her with concern.

'Oh, you're safe, you're safe,' she whispered. 'How worried I have been about you.'

'I-I . . . saw you in Svengejar,' Marina stuttered.

'Me? In Svengejar? But what nonsense. I am here, dear heart. And thank goodness I am! Even a few more moments and you would have . . .' She tucked the fur tighter around Marina's neck. 'You silly little fool. Don't you know that the winter this far north will eat you?'

'My father . . .' Marina's head felt heavy. The relief of seeing Miss Smith gave her body permission to feel unbearably tired. If only she could lie down. She closed her eyes.

'Your father?' Miss Smith shook her slightly. 'But he is in Cadiz on the HMS *Neptune*. You told me yourself.'

'No . . .'

'The *Neptune* is not in Spain?'

'It is.' If only she could sleep. 'But my father is on a different boat. It's a fishing boat. And he's come north. That's how I saw you – in Svengejar – I got off the *Sea Witch* because I saw you on the docks. Your hood was up, but your hair had come loose. You were running through the streets. A short skirt and boots. You had gone to meet someone. I was just about to call out when—'

'Does your head hurt? You seem to be saying such strange things.' Miss Smith did not say anything about Svengejar.

Marina felt confused. 'But what are you doing here?'

Miss Smith's beautiful pale forehead creased in a frown. 'We keep a sonar transmitter on this island. An enemy spy has come to steal it.'

Where was her father? He had come to repair some old sonar transmitter and yet he had unwittingly wandered into a landscape of enemy spies. 'I have to find my father,' Marina said.

'What do you mean, you have to find your father? You said he was on his boat.'

'But he went to the whaling station. He hasn't returned. And now the *Sea Witch* has left for Portsmouth. But I couldn't leave my father here, alone.'

'Let me help. How long ago did he leave?'

'Two days ago.'

'What time?'

'Eleven hundred hours.' Marina sniffed.

'There, there, don't fret. Your father is an exceptional naval officer. Why, they have yet to invent a situation that he can't get himself out of. But still. We must move quickly. How fortunate that I am here, just in time.' She turned away to the other figure, who was waiting near a submarine for that is what the dark shape beneath the ice had been. 'Can you get my young friend something warm to drink? We still have a way to go and she's half frozen.'

The figure, his face obscured by goggles and the hood of a long fur coat, stepped forward. He reached into his pocket and brought out a hip flask, which he handed to Marina.

'Don't be foolish! You must help her. She's too weak to drink by herself.'

The man – Marina believed that it must be a man as the figure was so tall – put the flask to her lips. Whatever was inside was sweet and warm.

'It tastes of cherries,' she muttered.

'It's good, heh?' Miss Smith smiled. 'We can't get any closer to the whaling station in my submarine: the underwater channel has already frozen. So now we will go the rest of the way on foot. My manservant will bring everything we need. He's immensely strong and will not tire. We will move quickly. You will see.'

The servant now pulled on a set of loose white clothing over the top of his furs. He strung a rifle over his shoulder. He then dragged a sledge and some long pieces of wood from the submarine's gaping mouth. Marina watched as Miss Smith strapped the pieces of wood to her boots and laced them around her ankles. The man handed Miss Smith two poles, and indicated that Marina should sit on his sledge before wrapping her in more fur.

Paddy growled.

'He won't hurt you,' Marina said, weakly.

The manservant picked Paddy up and tucked him in with Marina. 'He likes you,' Marina said to the silent man. And it did seem that Paddy looked up at the man with grateful eyes. And then the brave, tired dog sighed and settled his head against Marina's chest, and yowled that he hoped she would find him an effective blanket.

The manservant strapped two pieces of wood to his feet, slipped a leather harness over his shoulders and started to move forward on his skis. Miss Smith took her lipstick out of her coat pocket and painted her lips. That seemed an odd thing to do in the middle of that desolate place: it was like watching a dark red rose bloom in the snow.

'Tallyho!' Miss Smith cried to the open, cold, star-filled sky. And she set off with loose-limbed speed.

26

Miss Smith glided ahead. Marina, tucked under a pile of furs on the sledge, Paddy's head on her chest, gave in to the rhythmic movement of being dragged over the snow. The landscape, which before had felt so hostile, now seemed beautiful. Stars quivered overhead and the snow glistened. 'We're safe,' she whispered to Paddy as she touched the frost flowers on the furs. 'And Miss Smith will help us find Father and your friends. We'll soon all be together again.' She stroked Paddy's ear and he sighed contentedly.

Perhaps Marina dozed, because when she opened her

eyes she saw a group of huts on the horizon. Lights shone like pillars into the sky.

As they came closer, Marina saw the huts were surrounded by large coils of wire. There was a sentry box at the edge of the compound. Miss Smith signalled to her manservant to halt the sledge while she approached the sentry, also dressed in a loose white uniform, the hood pulled up against the biting cold. After a brief exchange, the man saluted Miss Smith, who then waved her manservant on. The sentry stood to attention as the sledge slid past.

Beyond the sentry box, more white-suited figures were pushing wooden cases on rollers across the ice. Light spilled out from the huts, and Marina heard a blur of male voices.

The Admiralty base looked well guarded, well maintained and well provisioned. Of course this must have been why her father had been able to travel so lightly and had not needed decent food for the journey. Once here, he could have expected a good meal for him and his dog team and even, perhaps, a bed to sleep in before he started his journey back to the *Sea Witch*.

The *Sea Witch*. Where was she now?

The sledge stopped outside one of the huts. Paddy lifted his head and sniffed the air. Miss Smith had bent over to unstrap her snow equipment and the manservant took off his leather harness. He stepped forward, the wind screaming, and opened the door.

'Hurry,' Miss Smith said. 'We must get you out of this cold.' Her face was as bright and white as the snow, her eyes glittering.

Marina dragged a sleepy Paddy into the hut. The manservant pulled his sledge away and Miss Smith closed the door on the wind. She quickly lit the oil lamps and placed more logs in a small iron stove. The room was furnished with comfortable armchairs and white bearskin rugs, a bookcase and a large painting of a medieval castle on a hill. It was just the sort of room that Marina would have wanted for herself – if someone had taken away the rugs. Perhaps soon her father would be here to join her and they could sit with Miss Smith and talk for a while before returning to London.

'I hope Father will be here soon.'

'I have ordered the sentry to send out search parties.' Her voice was calm and reassuring. 'If your father is anywhere on this island, we will find him. Sit down – please, make yourself comfortable. I'm sure we won't have long to wait.'

Marina sank into one of the armchairs and Paddy flopped down at her feet. 'Now put your feet on that little brass box on the floor,' Miss Smith instructed. 'It's a charcoal burner. 'You can't always tell how cold you are. Your father, when we've found him, will not be very pleased with me if I return you to him without several toes.'

'I don't feel the cold,' Marina said. But Miss Smith smiled and wagged her finger and came and lifted Marina's feet on to the little box. A delicious warmth flowed up through the soles of her boots.

'I won't allow my friends to get cold.' Miss Smith patted her hand.

'My father didn't mention that he was travelling to anywhere like this,' Marina said. 'He said that he needed to take everything with him for his journey. He was going to eat only the food he took with him and sleep in a tent on the snow.'

'Perhaps your father did not realize that since he was last here, the whaling station has become so important to the navy. Fifteen years ago, there was just one hut. But now we have a hundred men stationed here. We need facilities for them. Men work better when they are well rested and well fed. Tell me –' Miss Smith raised an eyebrow – 'does your father still eat that awful mix of grease and dried meat?'

Marina pulled the calico-wrapped ball out of her

231

pocket. 'Pemmican? Cook says it tastes like Christmas dinner when you're cold and hungry.'

'Urgh.' Miss Smith wrinkled her nose. 'Your father always likes to do things the hard way.' She took off her coat and sat down on the chair opposite Marina. She was wearing a dark uniform: a narrow-cut jacket with gilt buttons over a skirt that stopped well short of her ankles. She stretched out her legs and placed her white boots next to Marina's feet on the charcoal burner. 'He once spent a year rowing himself round the coast of Choseon.'

'How do you know that?' Marina asked.

'I read his files, don't forget. My work at the Admiralty means I know all sorts of things about the men who sail the world for the king . . .' She smiled and her cheek dimpled. 'And I have had a fascination with your father's work for as long as I have worked in the office of the First Sea Lord. Which is why I was so surprised about this latest jaunt of his.' Miss Smith pulled off her sealskin gloves, frowning slightly.

'Do you think it will take long to find my father?' A faint prickle of fear. Could her father have got lost? Perhaps Marina should be outside, joining the search party.

'The men will turn the island upside down, if

necessary, to find him. They'll pick him up soon. Let me make you some tea while we wait.'

She stood up and poured water from a pretty silver kettle sitting on a stand above a spirit light into a teapot on the stove, and added tea leaves. She dropped sugar cubes into an enamel mug with sugar tongs shaped liked claws. The tea tasted sweet and smoky.

'So warming,' Miss Smith said as she took a sip from her mug. 'Now, why don't you tell me about your accidental trip to Pechorin Island? Just how did you find your way on to the ship? I was so anxious about you when I saw that the *Neptune* had left and yet my dear little friend was nowhere to be seen. I can't imagine what your father must have said when he saw you. Such a strange idea of his, to take a small fishing vessel on this trip. Anyone would think he didn't want us to know he was coming...'

Marina enjoyed talking to Miss Smith. The young woman listened so carefully, unlike Ivy, who only ever gave her half her attention. Or her father, who had rarely listened at all. Marina felt herself glow as she told Miss Smith about what an important member of the crew she had become, how she had named all the dogs, seen whales, and even plucked a flying signals device out of the sky. Miss Smith was fascinated and asked question after question. No detail of Marina's life on the *Sea Witch* seemed too small.

'The *Sea Witch* has the same class of engine as a gunboat? But that must make her very fast! No wonder Commander Denham was able to survive the storm and get to Pechorin Island so quickly!'

She leant forward. 'Now, tell me about the storm. There was no warning. It seemed to come from nowhere. Oh, I was so relieved to be beneath the waves, where no storm can find me! But if I had thought that my dear friend Marina Denham was being tossed from here to there on those brutal waves above me, I wouldn't have been able to sleep a wink. *How* did you survive?'

'My father is extremely brave,' Marina said, feeling immensely proud. Now here was a story which would impress Miss Smith. She just must not think of how she had felt as she had stood on the prow of the boat and felt she had become the sea. That was too foolish. 'He called us all into the mess . . .' Marina explained.

'And the dogs survived their ordeal in the hold?' Miss Smith's eyes flickered with concern.

'They did!'

'And not one man was lost! Remarkable!'

Marina squirmed. 'Almost no one.'

'Almost?'

Marina faltered as she described the loss of Trenchard. 'He was very brave. But he didn't follow orders, you see,' she muttered, staring down at Paddy's head.

Miss Smith shook her head. 'Tragic,' she whispered. 'To be drowned at sea must be the most horrible way to die. But this man, this Trenchard, did not obey orders. What could he expect? This is why I only work with men I really trust. If a man does not follow my orders, I dismiss him. On the spot.' Marina was impressed that the First Sea Lord's secretary was given so much responsibility. The woman must be extremely capable. And to think that the navy didn't want to employ such women! 'My manservant, for example, he follows my every command. Do you know? I really think he would die for me . . . not that I would ask him to!' She patted Marina's hand once more. 'Now, dear heart.' Her eyes twinkled. 'A welcome feast for my friend.'

27

Miss Smith rang a small bell and two men appeared and laid a table with a starched white cloth, cutlery and several silver-lidded dishes. After they were dismissed with a wave of Miss Smith's hand, she lifted one of the domed lids and sniffed appreciatively.

'This is my favourite dish of roast pork,' she said. 'Quite delicious after a long trek to the most northerly part of Pechorin Island. And with the pork, some fried potatoes, pickled cucumber and sour cream. Have you ever tasted this dish before? I think perhaps not. In London the potatoes are so sad and plain – boiled until they are grey. These, I think, you will like much more.'

Miss Smith placed a plate piled with food on Marina's lap. Paddy looked up hopefully and Marina slipped him a fried potato. Marina wasn't sure she would like anything as strange as pickled cucumber, and she didn't think Ivy would approve of the mound of cream on her plate, but she took a mouthful. It was delicious, and she took another and another.

'You like it?' Miss Smith was watching her, smiling. She took the cork out of a bottle of wine and poured the golden liquid into a glass.

'Oh, I do,' Marina answered, still chewing. What could Ivy say? She was in Kent, with her sister! While Marina was safe in this Admiralty hut with her glamorous friend, Miss Smith, waiting for her father. How surprised he would be to see her . . . Marina swallowed.

'Is this what you used to eat in Northumbria?' She felt she must say something, as the woman was watching her as if she wanted Marina to talk. 'Where you said you grew up?'

'How clever you are to remember!' Miss Smith took a sip of her wine. 'This recipe is indeed a favourite in my home town.' She smiled indulgently at Marina. 'When I knew I had to come here, I made sure to send my favourite food so that I wouldn't feel homesick. What is the food that would most remind you of your home?'

Marina thought of Ivy's dry bread-and-butter pudding, the custard often lumpy and not enough of it. Or the watery cabbage that was served, without fail, with a slice of gammon every Thursday. But how could she admit that Ivy was not just a 'plain' cook, but a bad one as well? That a crust of bread and beef dripping was by far the nicest supper Marina ever ate. It felt that she was being disloyal to tell Miss Smith of Ivy's failings.

'Eclairs,' she said, choosing an impressive lie rather than the boring truth. 'I have two every day for breakfast. With a hot chocolate. It's quite the nicest thing. Sets me up for the day.'

'Eclairs?' Miss Smith's eyes widened in surprise. 'And hot chocolate? Before noon? What a constitution you must have!' And then she laughed. 'That's quite the most decadent thing I have ever heard. I must try it! Now. Eat up. I can't offer you an eclair, but there will be a slice of chocolate cake for pudding, *if* you clean your plate.'

Marina redoubled her efforts, piling potatoes on to her fork.

'Oh, I'm so happy that I found you. I hadn't realized how good it is to have a dear friend with me. I hadn't realized how very lonely I can be.' Miss Smith leant forward to whisper, even though the only other person in the room was Marina. 'To have a female companion means that I can talk so much more freely. Men are so dull, don't you think? How bored you must have been on the *Sea Witch*. How much more fun we would have had in my little submarine! Would you like to come with me next time?'

'Oh, yes!' Marina gasped, her mouth full of fried potatoes. She chewed furiously so that she would be ready to answer another question.

'Perhaps I should ask for an assistant,' Miss Smith mused. While she had been speaking, she had taken out a small cigarette case from her bag. She flipped it open, selected a cigarette and lit it, using a lighter shaped like a tiny pistol. Marina was shocked. She had never seen a real, live woman smoke; only the photographs of 'new women' in the *Society News*. Miss Smith looked like a beautiful Medusa as she leant back in her chair, coiling snakes of smoke around her head. 'It would need to be the right person, of course. Someone very young, who I could train up. And they would need to be bright and brave . . .'

'And loyal,' Marina added, helpfully.

'And loyal, of course.' Miss Smith smiled. 'Perhaps a girl, no, a *young woman*, –' Miss Smith nodded at

Marina – 'who has proved herself able to survive in inhospitable and desolate places. A young woman who has trained herself to notice details others would dismiss as unimportant. A young woman I could call my friend.' She looked at Marina as she blew more smoke from her lipsticked mouth.

A shrill ringing sound. 'Ah!' Miss Smith jumped up and snatched a handset from a wooden box fixed to the wall. She held the trumpet-shaped earpiece to her head, turning away from Marina as she listened intently to what was being said. When she turned to Marina, her face blazed with happiness. 'He's been found!' she declared.

'My father?'

'He will be with us shortly. I am just having my medical officer look at him.'

'He's not hurt?'

'He's a strong man, but he has been on the ice for over two days. It's best that we check him over. Now. Why not have that piece of chocolate cake while we wait?'

Marina thought that it would be rude to disagree.

'Simple pleasures,' Miss Smith sighed as she handed Marina a slice of cake on another plate. 'You must remember these moments, Marina. Two dear friends in the warmth of this hut, waiting for the safe return of your father.' She looked grave, her voice became serious. 'You know there will be a war very soon.'

'It's what my father thinks.'

'The British navy is preparing for it. The Mordavians, too, have built a powerful navy. This war will be lost or won at sea.' She frowned. 'Tell me, did your father ever talk of a sonar transmitter on Pechorin Island?'

'I . . . I . . . don't remember.' Marina felt awkward, suddenly. Was this something she could talk about with Miss Smith?

'Oh, do try. Perhaps he mentioned something? A machine that could send a signal through the water that no one could intercept?'

Marina knew nothing of the sonar transmitter on the island other than that it was broken and needed mending. What should she say?

'Perhaps he could not tell you,' Miss Smith continued. 'The transmitter is secret, after all. The British navy's greatest discovery – did you know that? And all the work of your father!'

The door swung open. Paddy jumped up and gave a sharp bark of warning.

'Shhh.' Marina held him by his harness. She turned

to the door. 'Father?' she cried out in surprise.

Had the search party got the right man?

The man who stood in the doorway did not look like her father. This man looked as if he'd been shipwrecked. His fur coat was gone. His hair stood up on end, his beard was unkempt and his clothes were dishevelled, the sweater torn at the sleeve. He cradled one arm in the other as if it caused him great pain. A large purple bruise bloomed on his cheekbone and his lip was swollen and split.

'Marina?'

'Come in, come in.' Miss Smith waved to Commander Denham. 'We're so pleased we have found you.'

Marina grabbed her father's coat and pulled him into the warmth of the room. He looked dazed, as if he had just woken up and couldn't understand how he had arrived in this cosy place after the barren iciness of the island.

'But how are *you* here?' her father asked, looking at Marina intently. 'I left you on the *Sea Witch*.'

'I had to come and find you, Father.' Marina sniffed. Her father looked so unlike himself she thought she might cry. That would be too awful for Miss Smith to see. She might think that Marina was not the sort of girl she would pick for her assistant.

'Commander Denham.' Miss Smith lightly touched Marina's head in a comforting gesture. 'I'm so pleased that we found you. Marina was out of her wits with worry. I must tell you that your daughter is quite the bravest girl I have ever met. To leave her boat and come and find her father! You should be proud of her.'

Commander Denham blinked, still seemingly confused.

'Would you like some food?' Marina tugged at his arm. Now she had him with her, she didn't want him to only talk to Miss Smith; she wanted some of his attention for herself. 'It's quite delicious. There's some meat, and it's not at all like Ivy's chewy cutlets. It's a special recipe. From Miss Smith's home town.'

Her father looked down at her as if he wanted the answer to something very important. 'And where would that be, Marina?'

'Somewhere in Northumbria.' Marina then leant in and whispered, 'That's why she speaks with a funny accent.'

'I'll take some, thank you,' he said. 'If Miss Smith has any to spare.'

'Always so polite.' Miss Smith smiled as Marina heaped food on to a plate and handed it to her father. 'There's wine, too.'

243

Marina sloshed some wine into a glass.

'Tell me, Miss Smith –' Marina's father looked around the hut for the first time – 'where did you find my daughter?'

'Oh, I think we found each other. You should have taken care of her and not allowed her to wander off on the ice shelf. You should be grateful I found her when I did, Commander. Marina is very lucky to have survived such conditions.'

Her father took the glass from Marina's hand and, clearly thirsty, finished it in one gulp. 'And how did you get here?'

'Miss Smith was given a submarine by the Admiralty,' Marina interrupted. 'Oh, Father, I was so very scared. Paddy and I had got so tired – I think Paddy was still not at his best after he was so sick, and we had to stop and rest. But he loves the taste of pemmican. I was so worried that we would run out of food before we found you . . .'

'How did you get so far?'

'I made a sledge. Out of a packing crate.' It seemed odd that her father didn't look proud of her. Surely he should be pleased that he had such a brave and resourceful daughter? 'I saw a black shape under the ice. I thought it was a snow spirit coming to eat me.' She laughed at her own stupidity, but her father didn't seem to find it amusing.

'What do you make of the old whaling station, Commander Denham?' Miss Smith filled her guest's glass with more wine. 'Wasn't this place, and all that was found here, your discovery?'

'It was just an old whaling station,' her father muttered.

'And yet you spent a whole winter here fifteen years ago. I wonder what it was that kept a man of your intelligence and talent and ambition so entranced?'

Marina's father said nothing.

'I was intrigued by your mission here.' Miss Smith turned to Marina. 'Did you know about your father's time on Pechorin Island? Perhaps he never told you. He brought a crew of men to survey the island's coast. Spent long, dark months up here with not enough rations. When he returned, he reported the survey was complete. And yet I have not been able to find any of the maps he said he had made at the Admiralty. And, believe me, I have looked. Yet your father is a thorough man, Marina. These missing charts made me believe that whatever he had found on Pechorin Island, he wanted to be forgotten.'

'Perhaps there wasn't anything here,' her father said.

Miss Smith laughed. 'Oh, I think there was.'

'How would you know which maps the Admiralty keeps? Even a secretary to the First Sea Lord can't get access to those files.'

'Oh, you'd be surprised how I squirm and wiggle my way into all sorts of files and archives.' Miss Smith smiled. 'I found your expedition files, of course. From what I remember, you had made a plan of the town of Windsor but the writing was in Muskovite. Anyone glancing at it might think it was indeed a survey of Pechorin Island. And that's what aroused my curiosity. Of course, it could have been a joke, but you are a serious man. So I set out to discover why you were so keen to cover up what you found here.'

'And what had I found here?'

'We both know that.'

'And what are you doing here?'

'I am carrying on with the work that you started. I found the sonar transmitter, you see . . . Of course, you know it's quite broken. Such a delicate instrument. I think I was too heavy-handed.' She pulled a mock sad face. 'Whoops.'

'It's not yours . . .' Commander Denham whispered.

'It wasn't yours, either. But what does it matter? It's broken. Beyond repair.'

'I'd like to see it.'

'I don't think that's wise, do you?'

'But my father can mend the transmitter!' Marina blurted out. 'That's why he's come to the island, Miss Smith!'

The woman smiled kindly at Marina. 'He's a little late for that. But it hardly matters, as I have a new transmitter that is so much better. It's much easier to control. And, I believe, under the right circumstances, its signal could be much stronger.'

'You are mistaken, Miss Smith. There is no other transmitter.'

'Perhaps you have forgotten, Commander. I don't make mistakes.'

A clock struck the hour. Marina, after the exertion of her journey, the large meal, the warmth of the room and the relief of seeing her father, could not ignore her tiredness. She stifled a yawn. Seeing this, Miss Smith said, 'You need to get some rest, both of you. Oh, and no need to take your luggage with you, Commander.' She glanced at the Commander's kitbag. 'We can supply everything you need.'

'Thank you, but I'll keep my bag.'

'So heavy!' Miss Smith had grabbed the kitbag and pulled the cord at its neck. 'What do we have here?' She tipped the contents on to the floor. 'Ice shoes and rope and –' she bent down and picked up a leather mask and a length of rubber tubing – 'underwater breathing equipment? Why, Commander Denham, what is the meaning of this? Anyone would think that you wanted to go for a swim! Anyone would think that the sonar transmitter you came here to mend was situated under the water!'

'*Please*, Miss Smith!' Commander Denham begged. Marina could not understand what had made her father look so desperate.

Miss Smith raised an eyebrow and shrugged. She kicked the mask to one side and frowned. 'You're in such a bad mood, Commander. I've found your daughter for you after you were so careless as to leave her behind. I might have expected you to be at least a little grateful. Why, I am even considering asking her to become my assistant and work with me on the sonar transmsitter.'

'You wouldn't.'

'But your daughter is so talented.'

'She is not!' Marina's father said, vehemently.

'Such a bad attitude; your daughter is quite the most talented girl I have ever met. Why doesn't she show you? She has a lovely voice. She told me so herself. It's just like her mother's.'

The rich meal Marina had eaten seemed to turn into a large stone in her stomach. She didn't want to sing in front of Miss Smith. She had no singing voice at all. Why had she lied?

'She doesn't want to sing.'

'*Such* a spoilsport, Commander. But perhaps you are just tired.' She reached out and pressed a bell. 'I will have you taken to your quarters.'

'Good night, Miss Smith,' Marina said, embarrassed by her father's rudeness. 'Thank you so much for all you've done for us. My father and I are extremely grateful.' She pulled Paddy up from the floor. He stretched and then looked up at Marina hopefully. She was going to ask if she could take another piece of pork for the dog, but Miss Smith had already turned away.

28

A man in uniform appeared and indicated that they should follow him. Marina and her father stepped out of the warmth of the hut. The sky trembled above them. Marina wanted to link arms with her father and help him along in the snow – he was limping slightly – but his sullen mood made her draw back. Paddy sniffed the air and yowled.

'Where are your dogs?' Marina asked, looking around.

'Miss Smith will no doubt look after them,' her father muttered.

'Father, are you in pain? Should you ask to see the medical officer again?'

'That's one person I'll be happy never to set eyes on again. But if I do, I'll make sure to knock his block off.'

They trudged across the compound. Men were loading crates on to sledges. Horses with thick blankets thrown over them waited patiently to pull them away. Searchlights swept across the snow. A siren went off and Marina heard the sound of drilling.

The door to a small hut was unlocked. The man stood aside for them to enter. The room was very different from the cosiness of Miss Smith's quarters. But then, thought Marina, Miss Smith had not expected guests. Perhaps those two narrow metal bedsteads with bare mattresses and thin grey blankets rolled up was all that was available. Even after the man lit an oil lamp, the room looked as bare as a cell. Would Miss Smith's room be so sparsely furnished? Marina wondered.

Left alone, Marina's father sank down on the bed. 'Why didn't you do as you were told, Marina? Why didn't you stay on the *Sea Witch*?'

'Because Finchin gave the order to leave. Brown had pulled up the anchor and the Chief Engineer had started the engines. Finchin was leaving you.'

'He was following orders.'

'But what good is that if it means he leaves you to freeze to death?'

251

Paddy whimpered and lay down on the floor at the Commander's feet. He put his head between his outstretched paws and looked up at Marina, as if he, too, was anguished at what she had just said.

Marina knelt down and put her arms on her father's knees. 'I couldn't stay on the boat knowing you were missing. I know what it feels like to be left alone, and I didn't want you to ever find out.'

'Oh, I know what it's like to be left alone, Marina,' he muttered.

'But now we're together. We're here. We're safe. And Miss Smith won't let anything bad happen to us!'

He raked his hand through his dishevelled hair. 'Oh, what's the use? It's all finished.'

A chill clutched at Marina's bones. What was her father talking about?

'But Miss Smith has rescued us.' Her heart raced. This was not how she imagined her meeting with her father would be. He should have hugged her and told her he loved her and that he was proud of her for being so brave. Surely no other girl would have made a sledge and followed their father across the ice shelf? Marina felt very small and very stupid. Would her father never be proud of her, whatever she did? Miss Smith had seen that she was talented and brave. Miss Smith said that they were friends and hinted that Marina could be her assistant even though she was so young. Why could her father not see how special she was?

'I thought I could keep you safe and happy and well,' he said. 'I couldn't do that for your mother, but I thought I could do it for you. And now ... now ...'

'Don't worry, Father.' Marina stroked the arm of his sweater. The wool had come unravelled and it was damp. 'I'm quite safe now I'm with you. It's just that you're so tired after your journey. Why don't you lie down and sleep? And then, when we wake up, Miss Smith will help us get home.'

Her father said nothing; he seemed lost in his own thoughts. And then, without warning, he lay down on his narrow bed, facing the wall.

'You're right, Marina,' he said, quietly. 'Forgive your poor father. I forgot how this place makes a man feel. Memories of another mission. Hopes for the future. It all gets into such a muddle in my mind. My body aches all over. I'm so tired. I'll have forty winks ...' He yawned. 'Yes, I'll just have a nap, and then when I wake up, everything will seem very different.' He pulled off his boots and put them neatly by the bed. Then he lay down once more, pulling the thin grey blanket over himself.

'Marina?' he whispered. 'I'm sorry I haven't always

been the best of fathers. I'm sorry I've spent so much time at sea. But things will change. I promise.'

'Father?'

'Yes?'

'What happened here all those years ago?'

He took a while to answer. Marina curled herself up at the bottom of his bed.

'I had read about this land in a book I found in the library when I was a student.' His voice was calm and quiet and made Marina think of the time she'd had chicken pox – she'd been allowed a fire in her bedroom and the Commander, on a rare trip home, had read stories to take her mind off her itching skin. 'It told of a land so far north it had been forgotten. I wanted to see that world made of winter for myself. I wanted to see the waters of an ancient sea so deep that it had been drowned by ice . . .'

Marina thought she could see her father, younger and less sad than he was now, sitting in a small hut with his men. They would have been surrounded by snow and wind and she knew that they'd had very little food. The ice shelf beneath her groaned.

'We were so hungry,' he went on. 'And so cold. We didn't know if we would survive . . . but then, one night, while we were sleeping, a fabulous feast appeared. And the next night and the next . . . The men thought it was spirit food, thought they would be enchanted if they ate it. But I didn't care.'

Marina's eyelids drooped, her limbs became heavy; she couldn't move them even if she wanted to. Perhaps she, too, had eaten enchanted food. Perhaps Miss Smith was a spirit who could enchant anyone she chose. Marina hoped she would be the one to be chosen . . .

In that sparse hut, in the middle of a barren island, Marina felt that her future life might, with the aid of Miss Smith, be rich and wonderful and full of great achievements. Her father might not believe in this possibility, but once he was rested, Marina would convince him. He had behaved rudely, and not been at all grateful to Miss Smith for saving him, but that was just fatigue after his arduous journey. In the morning, all would be different: her father would help Miss Smith with her important work. And – somehow – Marina would convince him to let his only daughter work for the beguiling secretary of the First Sea Lord.

Marina hugged her knees to her chest in excitement as she imagined how Miss Smith would come to rely on her. How they would travel together. How their work would save lives.

How could her father refuse her such a life?

29

The door rattled and then swung open. Cold wind barged in. Marina, sleepy, looked about her. Why did she have to wake up?

'What's happening?' she muttered.

A young man with plump pink cheeks, dressed in a smart grey uniform, stood holding a tray with two tin mugs and two large pieces of black bread. He took one look at Marina, placed the tray on the other bed and quickly left the room.

'Father?' Marina called out.

The door opened again but it was Miss Smith. She looked as if she'd been disturbed while she was getting dressed. She was wearing a white military-style jacket, on which she had pinned a scarlet silk rose, but she was still doing up the buttons at her wrist; her hair was only half pinned up.

'Marina. Where's your father?' Her voice was quick and urgent, but she smiled a bright, fleeting smile.

'I don't know.'

'Did he say where he was going? I've asked the man who was posted outside your door but he seems to know nothing.'

Marina shook her head. 'Should my father not have left the hut?'

Miss Smith slumped down on the empty bed and put her head in her hands. 'This is bad. I had hoped that once we'd found him and he was reunited with you, he would see there was no need to continue with his mission.'

'What do you mean?' Marina whispered, unnerved.

'Oh, Marina.' Miss Smith looked up. She blinked as if she had tears in her eyes, and pushed a coil of auburn hair from her forehead. 'I can't keep it from you any longer.'

'Keep what from me?'

Miss Smith looked suddenly careworn. 'I'm sorry to tell you . . .' She bit her lip. 'No child should ever hear such things about their father. But—'

'But what?' There was a second when all that Marina could hear was the groaning of the thousands of miles of ice around her.

'I have something I must confess, Marina. I lied to you. I told you that I was the Secretary to the First Sea Lord. But I am more than that: I, too, am a signals expert and I have been given the responsibility for running this station. It is a great honour and a sign of the trust placed in me. Even though my role is secret, others have found out. And they are jealous that I have been given such an important role in the defence of the nation. Your father is one of those men.' She sighed. 'Unable to accept that a woman could be as competent as any man, he came here secretly to try and ruin me and my work. He came here to sabotage the equipment I have here: my sonar transmitter.'

Of course. Miss Smith had not been a mere secretary, typing memoranda and sending messages. She was also responsible for running this station. Her father might not support such an important role being given to a woman, but he had not said that he had come to destroy the transmitter. Miss Smith must be mistaken. 'My father came here to mend the equipment. . .' Marina whispered.

Miss Smith shook her head vehemently. 'Remember I told you that there was an enemy agent on the island? That man is your father.'

The words were so shocking that Marina couldn't speak.

Miss Smith looked stricken. 'I had hoped that it wouldn't come to this. The sonar will be vital in the coming war. It will save the lives of thousands of sailors. But your father does not want me to have it.'

Marina tried to untangle her thoughts. 'But my father came here to mend the sonar transmitter,' she said again.

'That's what he told you. But, no. It is quite clear: he wants to sink the sonar transmitter to the bottom of the sea!' She shook her head. 'I thought that when he saw you yesterday, he would care enough about you to come to his senses and give himself up. But I was wrong. If a man doesn't care about his country or the crew he commands, why should he care about a child he scarcely sees?'

'You're wrong,' Marina managed to say. 'My father is no traitor.' Miss Smith's grave expression would surely break into a dazzling smile at any moment. Marina would have to tell her that the joke was not very funny, but they would soon be friends again.

No such thing happened.

Miss Smith stood up. 'I have known about your father's treachery for a long time. I want you to think, Marina, what your father has told you and how much of that has been lies. He said he was sailing on the HMS *Neptune* to Cadiz. But instead he sailed in an old fishing boat to Pechorin Island. And why would he come here?'

'To mend the sonar transmitter,' Marina muttered. Perhaps if she said it enough times, it would be true and she could ignore the creeping sense that Miss Smith was telling her a painful truth.

Miss Smith shook her head. 'But there is nothing wrong with the transmitter! In fact, I have improved it so that its signal can be directed wherever I want. Made the signal impervious to being jammed by the enemy. So why is your father here? I think it must be that your father does not want me to be successful. He wants to destroy my sonar transmitter and humiliate me.'

Marina sat on the bed and drew her knees up to her chest. She felt her body go very still. As long as she didn't move or react to what Miss Smith had told her, it couldn't be true.

Miss Smith sighed, as if she felt truly sorry for Marina. Then she stood up and went to the door. 'I'll get someone who will explain ... My manservant ...'

She spoke to someone outside. Her voice was clipped with anxiety. 'The room was not locked, despite my instructions, and now the Commander has gone.'

'I did lock the door,' a man's voice replied. 'But there are not many locks that could hold the Commander. And a guard is easy pickings for him. Whenever he's been locked up, he's escaped.'

A man now stepped into the hut. 'I'm so sorry that you've found out about your father this way,' he said, looking awkwardly at the floor.

Marina had never seen a ghost before. She was so shocked that she could hardly breathe. The man in front of her had taken off his submariner goggles and combed his hair. He smiled at her kindly, as if they were old friends. On his left cheek, a scar.

'Trenchard?' she whispered. 'Is it really you?'

'It was all part of my operation to understand your father's treachery,' Miss Smith explained. 'I knew there was an enemy spy working in the Admiralty, but I could not uncover the spy's identity. After I met you on the train and you told me about your father's trip to Cadiz, I knew something was wrong. Commander Barham was taking the *Neptune* to Cadiz, so what was your father doing in Portsmouth? And so I assigned

Trenchard to get himself on your father's boat at the last minute.

'He picked a somewhat dramatic way to leave, but I rose to the challenge and rescued him from the sea.' Her mouth flickered in a triumphant smile. 'I thought that your father might do something crazy – desperate men often do dangerous things – and I couldn't risk Trenchard's safety. Unlike your father, that is something I would never do.'

'I'm very grateful, Miss Smith,' Trenchard mumbled. 'I would have been fish food but for your skill as a submariner and your bravery in the sudden storm.'

'I saw you . . .' Marina whispered. 'I saw the shape of the submarine under the water when I fell from the winch. But no one believed me.'

Miss Smith ignored Marina's words and carried on talking in an urgent way about her father's treachery. 'I suspected your father for quite some time, but I had no proof. I really hoped that I was wrong.'

Trenchard nodded his agreement. 'Your father has escaped detection so many times before, Marina. He really is a very difficult man to catch. We even had gendarmes posted in Svengejar, hoping that we could catch him there . . .'

'It was *you* I saw Miss Smith talking to,' Marina said.

Trenchard shrugged. 'I had to keep in contact with Miss Smith. I had to tell her what I'd learned of your father's mission while I was on the *Sea Witch*.'

'But my father is a signals expert,' Marina blurted out. 'He came to Pechorin Island to mend some broken old equipment. He's no spy. He's no danger to anyone!'

'Can you be so sure of that? Can you be so sure that he has not come to destroy the powerful equipment I keep here?' Miss Smith asked.

'He wouldn't do such a thing.'

'It is troubling and upsetting, of course.' Trenchard sighed. 'You don't want to think badly of him – the Commander is your father. But ask yourself this. How well do you really know him? Can you trust a man who has lied to you so often in the past?'

'You hardly know him,' Miss Smith continued. 'After all, he has spent most of your life at sea.'

'My father wouldn't lie to me.' Tears sprang to Marina's eyes. Her father! A spy!

As if she had heard Marina's thoughts, Miss Smith said, quietly, 'You know it distressed me, too, that a man once so admired should be working for the enemy. And to think that he had access to so many secrets at the Admiralty. In the lead-up to war. And meanwhile I thought that he was a decent man.'

Miss Smith and Trenchard fell silent, as if over-whelmed at what they had said. Marina tried in vain to marshal her chaotic thoughts.

'I liked your father,' Trenchard told her, smiling sadly. 'Even now I find it hard to believe what he tried to do. I trusted him. Or, rather, he made me want to trust him. But I see now that he has been playing a part for many years.'

'It is because of your father,' Miss Smith said, 'that the enemy is preparing for war. They know that if your father succeeds in his mission, certain victory will be theirs.' But then her face brightened and she looked eagerly at Trenchard. 'Could we be wrong? Do you think that there's any chance at all that Marina is right and her father really came to mend the transmitter and not dismantle it?'

Trenchard frowned. He looked thoughtful. Marina's pulse rattled away as she held her breath. But then he shook his head and Miss Smith shrugged, defeated.

'I thought not.' She stood up, shoulders squared in determination. 'We must find the Commander. Before he can do any harm.' She took Marina by the elbow. 'Help me, Marina. We have to find him. Perhaps you can reason with him and convince him to give up his treachery, help him to fight for the right side.'

'What will you do with him?' Marina said. 'If you find him.' It was clear that her father had done something very serious and very wrong. 'Will you put him in prison?' She couldn't bear to be the person who helped Miss Smith find him if it meant he would be locked away, possibly for years.

Miss Smith's face creased in anguish. 'Prison?' She pulled Marina towards the door. 'He will be sentenced within the hour of his capture. He'll be shot moments later. It's the punishment for all traitors. Oh, don't look at me that way. You scare me.'

'You can't! You mustn't . . . He's a good man . . .'

'If only we can find him – stop him before he does something we all regret.'

'Will that help him?'

'I promise –' Miss Smith held both of Marina's hands tightly in hers. Her eyes flashed. Marina smelled a heavy perfume of gardenias. 'If you will help me find him before he wrecks my signals equipment – as heaven is my witness, I swear to you that I will stand before the judge and *beg* for his life.'

30

Outside the hut, men in white hooded jackets trimmed with fur were harnessing dog teams to sledges. Others were carrying skis and rifles. Beams of light lanced down from watchtowers. The wail of a siren. Miss Smith, holding Marina tight by the hand, ran across the snow, dodging the men. Those who realized who she was stood smartly to attention.

'They're sending out more men to find him,' she cried over the wind. 'Pray that we find him first.'

Trenchard was already waiting for them at the door to a small hut. Paddy had run after him and stood at his feet, panting.

Why were they going to that small hut? Her father would hardly be hiding there! Why were they wasting time?

Trenchard stepped in front of them and opened the door to reveal a metal grille, which he swung across, the metal screaming.

'Hurry,' Miss Smith cried. 'Into the lift. We will get to the transmitter quicker underground. I think that must be where your father has gone. He thinks he can still complete his mission.'

Trenchard swung the grille shut and in the next second the cage shivered and shook and started to drop slowly through the ice. Marina willed it to move more quickly. Her father was in danger!

Some moments later, the cage door was opened and they stepped out into an ice cave as long and as high as a cathedral. This space was illuminated by vast glass lanterns suspended from the carved arched ceiling on thick metal chains. In front of them, the entrances to a baffling number of ice passages branched off in every direction.

That there should be a whole network of tunnels beneath the ice: how would they ever find her father?

But Miss Smith did not hesitate. 'He will be at the transmitter station. That's half a mile yet. Can you manage, Marina?' Marina nodded. 'Well, come – and quickly. We don't have much time.'

They ran at speed through seemingly endless ice passages. Marina's thoughts battled to catch up with her feet. Only now could she begin to think about what Miss Smith had told her. But her chaotic thoughts made no sense: her father was no traitor. The woman must be wrong. But still, to excavate all these tunnels, the Admiralty must be doing something up here that was of great importance. Why did her father think he could break in and destroy their transmitter? Was he really working for the enemy? Oh, why couldn't Miss Smith have stopped her father before he left London if she really suspected him? It seemed beyond cruel to allow a man to attempt a crime that could have been stopped. And why? So he could be arrested and shot as a traitor? And what sort of man must Trenchard be, to spy on his fellow sailors? Didn't that make him just as treacherous?

Paddy ran just ahead of her, his gait smooth, his breathing regular. If only she had her sledge, they would have raced along.

The walls flickered with blue and silver lights: gases trapped inside the ice. What had the gases been called in the glass phials that powered the bird of ill omen? Philium and sentium. Very rare. How had the Mordavians got hold of such substances? Did they have their own supply? But Marina couldn't think of that now. Her legs hurt. The ice groaned. Marina's lungs burned with the effort of running. Oh, let them find her father before he was discovered. She would make Miss Smith understand that he was a good man. Mistaken, perhaps, but not someone who would ever do anything that would harm anyone.

Just as Marina thought that her legs or her lungs might give out, she caught the sharp tang of salt air. But they were meant to be going to a transmitter station, not the sea!

Miss Smith stopped running and put her finger to her mouth to show that they must be quiet. They crept forward, Marina holding her breath.

Ahead, at the mouth of the tunnel, a man-made ice jetty extended into a dimly lit cavern. Black seawater lapped at the icy walls.

This was not a transmitter station, and there was no transmitter to be seen. Had Miss Smith taken the wrong tunnel? Would they have to run back and start to look for her father in one of those other tunnels?

But Miss Smith stayed where she was. She did not

seem to think she was in the wrong place. She stared into the cavern.

On the jetty ahead of them, a solitary figure was crouched on the ice, bending over the water. His hair stuck up and his clothes were dishevelled. Marina saw the glint of a blade in the man's hand. He was sawing at ropes fastened to a large block of ice. But the work was hard: the knife was too small and too blunt.

A splash. A dark shape flicked out above the water and was quickly drawn back in. Could there be a whale in that water? But the cavern would be too small for such a creature. Perhaps it was a whale calf that was trapped.

'What's happening?' Marina clutched at Miss Smith's sleeve. 'You said my father would be in the transmitter station.'

Miss Smith seemed transfixed by Commander Denham's behaviour. 'But that's just where we are, Marina. And your father is trying to smash my transmitter.' She turned to face Marina, standing so close that Marina could feel the woman's warm breath on her cheek, smell that heavy scent of gardenias, so out of place in this cavern of ice. 'Can you be brave?' she whispered. 'Can you be braver than you've ever been in your life? It's such a lot to ask of you, but I must. If we are to save your father, I need to know that I can rely on you. That you are loyal.'

'I'll do anything to save my father.' Marina felt this so strongly that Miss Smith could have asked her to throw herself into the water and she would have done it happily. Now she finally understood what loyalty meant, what following orders meant. It was to save the lives of those you loved.

A flicker of a smile. 'We're a good team.' And she grasped Marina's hand in her own. 'Courage,' she whispered.

Miss Smith stepped forward, her chin tilted up. She looked determined and without any fear. She took a breath. She would speak and Marina hoped, passionately, that when she did so, her father – please, just this one time – would listen.

'Denham!' Miss Smith's voice rang out, clear as a bell.

Her father froze when he heard his name. But within seconds he started to saw even more frantically at the rope.

'Enough, Denham. Why don't you stop? You know it's over.'

Marina's head felt heavy. She looked at Trenchard to see if he, too, was confused – what was her father doing, and why they were standing next to the sea instead of in a room with a transmitter? Surely her father would not be in trouble. He had done nothing to any equipment. But Trenchard's face was blank, giving no indication of what was happening or her father's part in it.

And still her father feverishly carried on with his work, not bothering to look up. 'You know I won't stop.' His voice was breathy from the effort. 'I can't. This is what I came here to do.'

'It will end badly for your father if he doesn't stop,' Miss Smith whispered to Marina as she took another step towards the ice jetty. 'Commander Denham.' Her voice was softer, more pleading. There were tears in her eyes. 'For the sake of your country, stop this now. Admit your treachery and let me do what I can to make your sentence bearable. The high command will listen to me. They trust me. They might even let you slip away from here and let you go and buy a cottage in the countryside where you can live quietly and safely with your daughter.'

'Let me live quietly with my daughter? Oh, I think not! I think your high command has other plans for me!'

Miss Smith pulled Marina closer. 'Tell him,' she whispered. 'He must stop. He must. Or he'll be shot for treason. The guard will be here in just moments. They will arrest him. You must speak to him.'

What should Marina do? Her father was no traitor, she was sure. But what was he doing here? And what was he doing trying to cut through those ropes? What could be under the water?

'Marina,' Miss Smith urged. 'Please. Do what you can to persuade your father to stop. If you succeed, I will beg the Admiral to spare his life.'

'You'll let him leave here safely?' Marina whispered. 'And let us live somewhere safe?'

Miss Smith nodded.

Commander Denham gave a cry of frustration. 'Wait . . . Wait . . . Oh, just wait a while longer. I'm here. I'm here . . . Why won't this rope – argh!'

Marina stepped forward. 'Father?'

At the sound of her voice, her father's hands became still.

He groaned, 'No, no. Please. Not this.'

'Father, please stop. I don't know what you're doing, but you must stop now because . . . because . . .' Marina felt as if her tongue had swollen in her mouth. 'I don't think you are a traitor like Miss Smith says . . . So I want you to explain to her that you are not doing anything wrong. That you only want what's best for everyone.

And that this is just a misunderst—'

As she was speaking, her father turned slowly towards her. Marina was shocked at what she saw. A face so sad, so disappointed, so empty of any recognition of her that she took a step back. Miss Smith put her arm round her.

'There, there.' The woman stroked Marina's hair. 'It will soon be over. Your father will give himself up.'

The black water convulsed. Whatever was in the net was trying to free itself.

'Hush, hush,' Commander Denham said, as if speaking to the water. 'Forgive me. I tried my best.' And then he put his hands up in surrender.

'You knew, didn't you?' He looked broken. 'That no mission is worth my daughter's life. Her mother would never forgive me if I sacrificed Marina. She loved her so much. It broke her heart to leave her. She made me promise that I would do everything in my power to save our child and keep her safe.'

Miss Smith sighed. 'So noble, as ever, Denham.'

Paddy's fur bristled. He barked at the water. The black waves shivered.

'I'll come with you,' the Commander said. 'I'll hand myself in. Surrender. Accept any sort of justice you decide. But please . . . *I beg you* . . .' His voice broke.

'Don't hurt our daughter.'

'Father.' Marina felt relief flood through her. He had given himself up. Miss Smith would help him. Marina and he could be together and have the happiest of lives. 'Miss Smith doesn't want to hurt me. And she will help you. She will speak to the Admiralty and plead for your life.'

Instead of realizing that he was safe, her father looked heartbroken. 'But what if I don't want my life?'

Miss Smith took a deep breath, as if she were trying to ignore the man's ingratitude. 'You're such a fool, Denham,' she said calmly. 'You had the whole world in your grasp. For fifteen years, you have known of the existence of a transmitter so powerful that it would win any war.'

'Because I did not think this transmitter should be used as a weapon.'

What transmitter was this? Marina tugged on Miss Smith's arm. She looked at Trenchard, but his attention was fixed on the Commander.

'Don't hurt him, Miss Smith,' Marina pleaded. 'Can't you see he's not himself? Some sort of fever . . .'

'Imagine, Commander Denham.' Miss Smith's voice had a taunting quality. 'If only you had stayed away.'

'How could I?'

'You couldn't. You had to see your precious transmitter – the transmitter you discovered but let go – one last time before the war. Before I use it against the enemy.'

'You should not use the signal that way.'

Miss Smith shook her head. 'Even after my months of research, I have not discovered how the signal makes sailors so mad with grief they must drown themselves.'

'Only a demon would want to know.'

'You're a sentimental fool, Denham. In coming here to deprive me of my transmitter, you have instead brought me an enormous gift.'

'I've brought you nothing.'

Miss Smith's eyes sparkled. 'Imagine. If I had two transmitters! How much stronger would the signal be then?'

What was Miss Smith talking about?

'The transmitter you have in your possession was the last of its kind, you know that. The only one in existence.' Her father sounded defiant.

'I'm not so sure, Commander.'

'She won't sing for you!'

'Marina.' Miss Smith turned to her, took her hand in hers. Her eyes brimmed with tears. 'Can you see how unhappy your father is? He's lost his mind.'

'Stop, Gaby,' the Commander cried.

'Your father will have to be very brave if he is to convince the Admiralty to spare his life. Why don't you sing to him? Your mother did it once before.'

The water shivered, a wave leapt up over the ice and fell back.

'You won't make her.' Commander Denham took a step towards Miss Smith, his hands balled into fists. 'And even if you did, there's no boat for hundreds of nautical miles!'

'But what about the *Sea Witch*?'

'It left at 1100 hours yesterday.'

'But even so, I think Marina's voice is strong enough to reach them. And I am sure that your loyal crew would like to hear her song'

What was Miss Smith talking about? How could Marina's voice reach the *Sea Witch*?

'Don't sing, Marina,' her father pleaded. What was more upsetting than not understanding what this conversation was about was that her father was on the verge of tears. 'That's an order. As your Commander.' His voice broke. 'Please. I couldn't bear it for you to be responsib—'

'See? He's raving. He's lost his nerve,' Miss Smith whispered to Marina. 'You don't want the Admiralty to think he's a coward. We want him to be able to go before his judges with his head held high. To plead for his life as an honourable man, not as a gibbering wreck. Just sing a note or two. Your voice will raise his spirits. It will make him brave enough to face any danger . . .'

It was a strange request, but what could she do? Marina couldn't bear to see her father like this. He looked broken, scarcely her father at all. If she could help him get through this ordeal, give him enough strength to convince the Admiralty that he was no spy, had never had a traitorous thought in his body, it was worth him being angry with her for a few moments. She would gladly disobey an order to save his life. She remembered the song which Brown had sung on the *Sea Witch* and began, 'As I sailed out one day, one day.'

Her father put his hands over his face and groaned. 'Don't, Marina . . .'

A splash in the black water and then it went still as glass.

'Just another note or two,' Miss Smith urged her. 'And sing a little louder, do. You have such a pretty voice.'

'And being not far . . .' Marina swallowed. Her throat was dry. 'From laaaaaand.'

'No!' Miss Smith snapped. Her eyes flashed and her

beautiful, kind face was twisted in anger. 'That's not it!'

'Wh-what do you mean?' Marina stuttered.

'I told you, Gaby,' her father cried, his voice desperate. 'She doesn't know how to sing.'

Miss Smith's fingers dug into Marina's wrist.

'Ouch!' she cried. 'You're hurting me.'

'That's the wrong song.' Miss Smith spat the words in her face.

'I . . . I don't know any other,' Marina gasped. She tried to pull her arm away.

Miss Smith tightened her grip and twisted Marina's arm round. 'Sing the true song. The song your mother sang to you!'

'I don't know what you mean. I don't know any song. My mother had no voice!'

'No voice? Oh, your mother had a voice. Who do you think has sung those boats to the bottom of the sea? Whose voice has made those men so desperate they threw themselves off the sides of their boat, and gladly, too?'

'And yet you were not affected!' Denham cried out. 'You're so cruel that you could listen to the sounds of torture and not be driven mad!'

'I saw no tears in the water!' Miss Smith spat back, her voice harsh and unfeeling.

'You're heartless,' Commander Denham told her.

'So what? I don't care! I could listen to that thing down there make its sound every moment of every day and be unmoved. I rejoice that such a song can sing the British navy to its watery death – every last, miserable sailor.'

'Please let me go,' Marina begged. 'You're hurt—'

'Yes, I'll let you go. You're no use to me if you won't sing.'

'But I don't know how!'

'Don't know the song?' Miss Smith's eyes flashed with contempt. 'Little coward. You can learn the words down there!'

A sharp pain between Marina's shoulder blades. She fell towards the black water. She saw her father's anguish, saw him reach out to her. She lost her balance, couldn't right herself. A woman's laugh cascaded over her but was immediately shut out by the rush of ice-cold water.

31

Falling through the black depths of the water, Marina understood.

Her father was not the enemy. It was Miss Smith. She was the spy, the traitor working in the Admiralty. She had found out about a secret sonar transmitter. Her father had tried to hide its existence, but Miss Smith had found the fatal transmitter, planned to use it against the British navy in the coming war.

And Miss Smith had thought that Marina, too, could be such a transmitter . . . She had wanted to imprison her, torture her, force her to sing.

Marina looked up. Her father's face floated above her, his hand outstretched. She thought he might be calling her name, but the water blurred his voice. She didn't like to think of him being upset, but the water was so soft, like the most comfortable hammock, that she didn't think she could make the effort to climb back out. She smiled up at him, but he couldn't have seen, because he was shouting, pulling off his boots as if he would jump in after her. Trenchard dragged him back from the water's edge. Only Paddy remained, his odd-coloured eyes curious and unblinking. She was sorry to leave him.

Beneath her feet, infinite dark water. She felt so safe. This wasn't like drowning at all. She expanded her lungs and breathed in. This gave her such a thirst that she needed more. 'Goodbye, Father.' She tried to wave to him, but she was sinking lower and the ice cave was just a pale blur of light.

Down.

Down.

Marina saw ropes trailing through the water. She reached out to them. What were these for? They made her feel sad. Some poor creature must be caught in a net.

Within the net a sea creature with a beautiful, pale,

282

oval face; bruises bloomed like flowers on her translucent skin. Limbs – cut and bleeding – uncoiled. Black hair spread out like trailing seaweed. The face looked surprised at its own pain.

'I must free you,' Marina whispered, pulling at the knotted ropes. If Marina could not loosen them, the creature would die, suffocated in this cruel net. Her hands worked quickly; this was the knot her father had taught her – the pearl fishers' knot – designed to become tighter as the ropes swelled with water. She had never mastered it yet. But she had never really needed to. Now, it was essential that she make her fingers obey her. As Marina pulled and tugged, the ropes caused the creature more pain, and it twitched and tried to pull away. It shook its head, closed its eyes. 'But I need to help you,' Marina said. 'I need to set you free.' The creature went limp. Marina feared the worst, but now that it no longer fought Marina's efforts, the ropes slackened slightly and this was enough for Marina to gain purchase.

Miss Smith had called this creature a transmitter and had made Marina think what was beneath the sea was a signals machine, like the one on the *Sea Witch*. But Perkins' grandfather would have called it by another name. A mermaid. There was something else that

Marina realized too, with a sense of relief and recognition. It was something she had always known but not had the words to explain to herself. She knew this face. She recognized these eyes, lips and hair. This creature of the sea might well be a fatal transmitter whose signal was a song that could sing sailors to their death, but it was also a creature who had worn cruel black boots and sentenced itself to a life of silence. A machine or a mermaid. But Marina now sobbed another word for this rare, exquisite and tortured sea creature before her: 'Mother.'

The ropes came loose. Her mother sank down.

'Don't leave me,' Marina whispered.

The face – serene and no longer in pain – looked up. How could such a delicate creature exist away from the sea? Used to these dark waters, how the wind must have cut her face; how those huge eyes must have been blinded by the sun. Oh, and the pain in those legs, used to being carried by currents and waves. Each and every step must have been torture. What had brought her mother out of the sea? What had kept her away from the water so long?

Love for Patrick Denham had brought this mermaid up from her watery realm. And love for her child had kept her in his dry and dusty world. Marina had spent her childhood wondering why her mother had left her: the miracle was that her mother had stayed so long. Only a powerful love for her child could have kept her away from the sea, when every breath of air or step on land had been agony. Marina understood this without her mother saying anything.

'Let me come with you . . .' Marina held out her hand to try and catch those pale fingers. 'You don't need to be alone anymore. Let me come with you . . . to the Drowned Sea.'

It was unbearable. To find her mother and to lose her again.

Her mother must have felt the pain, too, because she pulled Marina close. And then Marina heard a wondrous sound: her mother was singing to her, and it wasn't a song of sadness and pain. The music, in all its shining complexity, was a song of becoming, a song of the ocean, a song of the self, and it was made from a language in which it was impossible to lie. This wondrous song was made from just one word: *Marina*.

Hours, days, or years later – Marina couldn't tell – the song came to its end. A single tear formed at the corner of her mother's dark, expressive eye – round and pale and translucent, like a pearl made from ice. Her mother took it in her slender fingers and held it out to Marina.

And the moment that Marina closed her hand round the precious gift, she felt herself pushed upwards on a rising current of water. She tried to resist, but the current was too strong. She looked down to see great gates swing open at the bottom of the sea – and beyond that, a beautiful, ancient sea garden. Her mother sank down through the gates, no longer in pain, no longer in anguish, but released from all care and suffering. The gates swung closed. Marina panicked. She wanted to be with her mother. But she could not get her body to stop floating upwards towards the light. A wisp of song as the gates locked. As the notes faded away, Marina realized that she could not follow her mother to that ancient, lost sea: her own skin was too warm for such icy waters and her eyes too bright for the dark.

The Drowned Sea would never be her realm.

A sharp pain in her chest. 'I must breathe!' she gasped. 'I must go home.'

She couldn't see her father. She couldn't see Paddy. Had they left without her?

'Wait!' she cried. 'Wait!

A black wet nose. Triangular ears of the softest fur. One blue eye, one brown, and a quizzical, curious gaze. 'Paddy?' Marina hugged the dog to her chest.

'Finally!' Jones's voice. 'You've decided to wake up.'

'But where am I?' Marina's head was heavy, as if it were filled with water.

'You're on the *Sea Witch*. Where do you think you could be?'

'But I was in the water . . . I fell in . . . I thought I would drown . . .'

'I knew you were still alive. I tried to get Finchin to understand, to stop him sailing back to Portsmouth, but he wouldn't agree. So I went to the Chief Engineer. I told him you couldn't have perished, see. You must still be somewhere on the ice . . .'

'How did you know that?' Marina looked up at him, his face intense, but proud.

'I could still hear your voice in my head.' He smiled. 'Remember I told you I'd lost the sound of my mam's voice? But not yours. I could still hear you, catch the tone of you . . . I just knew that we would find you if we turned back. The Chief Engineer agreed. We locked Finchin in his cabin. Turned the *Sea Witch* round.'

'You disobeyed an order?'

'I'm going to get it in the neck, I know,' Jones said, looking entirely thrilled at the prospect. 'Although Finchin agrees I was right. I don't think he's so angry with me. But, still. The navy can't have their men making up the orders.'

Marina uncurled her fist. There, lying in her palm was a large, translucent pearl.

Jones whistled in admiration. 'It looks like it's made of ice. It must be pretty rare, and probably worth a bit. No wonder you kept tight hold of it all the time you were ill.'

A pearl made from ice, Marina thought. Or perhaps a mother's tear.

Perkins poked his face into the door of the cabin. 'Commander! Come here! The little lady's awake!'

Brown now appeared, his face all smiles. 'Oh, but you gave us a real scare, old girl. Running off like that! Thought you'd caught it and no mistake.'

The men made way for her father. He smiled at her, and sat down on the bed and took her hand.

'What happened?' Marina asked 'How am I here? And not ...'

'Drowned?' her father asked. 'You got caught up in the ropes. Paddy got his teeth into the net and I managed to pull you out. Luckily you had only been in the water for a matter of seconds.'

'Seconds?'

'Of course. Had you been in the water any longer, you would have drowned. Even though we got you out quickly, you caught a terrible chill. We thought we'd lost you. You've been delirious for the last two days. Muttering about a song you've heard and saying your name over and over as if you were worried you'd forget it.'

'But . . . How did—'

'How did we get away from Miss Smith?'

Trenchard peered in. 'That might have something to do with me.'

'Stay away from me!' Marina cowered and tried to hide behind her father. 'You traitor!'

'Trenchard – a traitor?' Her father shook his head. 'Not at all. He's the most loyal man in the British navy!'

'But he was working for Miss Smith!'

'After a fashion. But he was mostly working for me. It never occurred to Miss Smith that if you rely on a traitor, that traitor might not be entirely honest with you!'

'Double agent!' Trenchard beamed. 'Waited all my life to say that. I mean, spying – that's pretty basic stuff. But once you're working for both sides, it takes it up to a whole other level!'

'We needed someone who could speak that tricky Mordavian tongue without an accent. And Trenchard had a Mordavian mother and an English father: it made him the perfect choice for someone Miss Smith thought she could manipulate.'

'So Miss Smith is Mordavian,' Marina whispered. 'She's not from Northumbria at all.'

'She tried, but she couldn't quite shift her accent,' Trenchard said, looking pleased with himself. 'Unlike me. I'm able to pass as a native in both worlds. Happy to eat pickled cucumbers and sour cream, but I do love roast beef and Yorkshire pudding!'

'But where is Miss Smith? How did we get away?'

Her father frowned. 'It was close, I don't mind saying. We left it all pretty late this time, heh, Trenchard?'

'Up to the wire, Commander. Once we got hold of you, Marina, I got a message to Jones to come and get us. Turns out they were already off the coast! We stole a dinghy and got away before the guards could stop us.'

'I'll be speaking to Jones about that later.' Her father frowned at Jones.

'When I heard that patrol come thundering down that tunnel, though, Commander –' Trenchard rolled his eyes – 'Marina in the water, you shouting your head off, Miss Smith screaming in triumph . . . I did think we'd blown it.'

'Miss Smith has a pair of lungs on her, it's true.'

'Oh, she screamed fit to burst all right when I called

my friends over to see her. She'd wanted them all locked up when you were found, sir. As if! I knew they'd be needed and had them positioned near the jetty.' He gave an ear-splitting whistle. 'Here they are!'

The dogs – Marina's dogs – all tumbled into the cabin in a confusion of wagging tails, fur and tongues.

'Miss Smith is a woman of many talents,' Trenchard explained over their yowling and panting and excited barks. 'She's an excellent spy. A luminous mind as well as charming and brave.'

'Why, Trenchard, I think you're sweet on her!' The Commander laughed.

'I might have lost my heart, it's true, if she weren't so damnably cruel. But how can an Englishman, even one whose veins are half-filled with Mordavian blood, love a woman who doesn't like dogs? Doesn't make sense! She was going to send these rascals to the firing line with your father! But, then, it turns out that dogs don't like her very much, either. And once Paddy got close, he showed her. With his teeth!'

'She did scream, rather,' Commander Denham commented.

'And dropped her pistol. She could hand out the pain, but couldn't take it.'

'And that gave us time to get you out of the water,'

291

Commander Denham said, smiling fondly at Marina.

'I tried to stay in the water,' Marina whispered. 'But my body wouldn't sink.'

Her father looked away, his expression pained.

Trenchard looked puzzled. 'Still feeling a bit odd?' he asked her. 'An icy sea is no place for a young girl!'

Could Marina tell them of what she had experienced beneath the water? Could she find the words? 'The sonar sank to the Drowned Sea,' she whispered.

'Er, you might say that.' Trenchard looked perplexed. 'Wherever it went, it won't be coming back. So that's mission accomplished, Commander.'

'We can get past the Mordavian battleships?' Marina asked.

'They don't seem so brave now that they've heard their transmitter is no more. And of course, there are eight of our boats coming to meet us. Although I doubt we'll need any help. I think we'll just have a grand escort back to Portsmouth.'

'What will happen to Miss Smith?'

Her father frowned. 'There is no Miss Smith, Marina. She is a Mordavian agent and spy, and married to the man in charge of the Mordavian navy. I think her husband will not be pleased with her. She promised him a transmitter that would win the war. He will hold her responsible for its loss.'

'It's probably safe to say that her life won't be all cherries and chocolate cake,' Trenchard added. 'Her husband is a cruel man. No idea why she took up with him, actually.'

What could Marina say? Miss Smith had said that she had wanted to choose her own life and not accept the narrow world she was offered. But her choices, while her own, were not right. Could there have been some other life that meant she could have been clever and brave but kind as well?

'So, I'd like to say that it's mission complete, Commander!'

'Indeed,' her father agreed.

'We're going home.' Marina let this thought sink in.

'We'll be in Portsmouth before the week is out. And then, young lady . . .' Her father gave her a stern look. 'No more gallivanting for you.'

32

Scratched arm, torn blouse. Marina looked down through branches dripping in golden leaves.

'Why so slow?' she called out.

'Give us a chance!' Owen's face, streaked with dirt, appeared below her.

'And still I'm last!' Edward gasped. He looked from Marina to Owen suspiciously. 'Did you cheat?'

'How is it possible to cheat?' Marina laughed. 'Unless you think that I used that pair of wings I have hidden in my pocket!'

'Wouldn't put it past you,' Edward muttered. 'I always said they would have burned you at the stake.'

'You're just a bad loser,' she said.

Marina reached and plucked some leaves for her Art in Nature class that afternoon. She would be making some sketches, and tomorrow she would start carving them in stone. Her weeks at this new school in the forest had awakened a passion for sculpture. 'Who could have known?' her father had remarked in his last letter. 'And is it true that Jones is allowed to crack codes and play puzzles all the time he's not outside?'

It was true. The headmaster was of the firm belief that young people should find the things that interested them and pursue them with as much energy as they could muster. His view was that it was easy enough for young people to follow their interests; nothing could stop them. But try and force them to sit still all day and learn Latin if their hearts weren't in it, and that spirit of curiosity and delight in application would be crushed. He set them interesting homework. 'Time Travel is Impossible. Discuss.' 'Time Travel is Possible. Discuss.' However, he was sensible enough to mind that the pupils in his care were thoughtful, kind and polite. He hated untidiness. He insisted that all of his pupils could do sums in their heads. He was fond of spelling tests, but they were the sorts of tests where you had to find the interesting words yourself and explain not just how you spelled them, but what they meant. He made the boys learn to make bread and the girls how to shoe a horse. He encouraged pets. The pupils and staff adored him. And it was at this school that Marina had convinced her father she would thrive. To his credit, her father had agreed. 'I am sorry that I almost sent you to that Ladies' College,' he told her. 'But I wanted to protect you.'

'I can do that myself. Or, at least, I have to learn how to.'

'You do. And if you make mistakes, you have to learn from them, too. I can't do that for you, nor is it right that I try.' He shook his head in amazement. 'Of course now I see this, it's a wonder I had been so mistaken for so long.' He smiled, a little sadly, then, 'I look forward to seeing what you can do with your life, Marina.'

Even better was the fact that Commander Denham – now in charge of Room 40 – had insisted that Owen, too, be taken on as a pupil and be prepared for exams that would see him have a career in naval intelligence.

The Commander wrote to Mr Jones to explain that his son had saved lives by not letting the *Sea Witch* return to Portsmouth. As a thank you, he was offering to pay for the boy's education. Mr Jones agreed, gratefully. But Owen was stubborn: his pride would not let him accept the offer of a place at the school in the forest. Only when his father pointed out that he could pay the money back out of his future naval salary did he accept.

Paddy barked at the sky. An airship floated serenely above. There was an army camp five miles down the road, and in the last few weeks the preparations for the war had intensified. Commander Denham's mission had been a success, but it was not enough. A long and bloody conflict between Britain and Mordavia was inevitable.

In the early days of the conflict, a Mordavian submarine caused great trouble in the northern seas, harassing gunboats and warships alike. There were rumours that this craft, so reckless, so remorseless in its pursuit of enemy boats, was captained not by a Mordavian officer, but by a female submariner.

This woman was written about in the newspapers, with a sort of grudging admiration for her demented mission to sink as many boats as possible. She became known as the Sea Witch, and every man in the British navy breathed more peacefully in their berths when she was captured.

The newspapers reported that, when caught, the

woman had to be forcibly dragged out of her submarine. She had then cowered before her captors, begging for mercy. 'A pitiful sight, she was bedraggled and barefoot,' the war correspondent wrote. He added that the submariner's red hair was unkempt and that she was 'more witch than woman'. But Marina knew that this was wrong, for Miss Smith would surely have climbed out of her submarine in her red boots and short skirt which showed an inch of calf; her lustrous auburn hair would have been artfully arranged, and her lips would have been curled in contempt and painted a scandalous red.

As the war dragged on, the stories of that dreadful, bitter conflict rushed towards the school in the forest and Marina's thoughts were taken up with the sadness of others. Edward's father joined the Artists' Rifles, a battalion of sculptors, painters and writers. He was killed one bright spring day in a terrible battle, alongside hundreds of thousands of other soldiers who lost their lives that day. A month later, the kindly Finchin, too, lost his life. Two kind, decent, talented men dying for king and country amongst an infinite sea of casualties. Such is the waste of war.

The bloody conflict broke the world as it had been:

change was violent and rapid. And in those years after her strange expedition on the *Sea Witch*, Marina prepared herself diligently, passionately, to claim her full part in this new world.

It wasn't always easy: she was often frustrated and confused. There were times when she forgot the language of herself, that secret language she had been given by her mother. And those were the most unhappy times in her life. But somehow, Marina always found a way back to remembering who she was and what mattered to her.

She would be a new sort of woman, she determined, twisting the ice pearl she wore, like a talisman, at her throat. She would treat everyone as equals and speak to them with courage, love and kindness; she would use that secret, lost, ancient language her mother had given her, to imagine and create a different sort of world.

There were others, too, who felt this new way of speaking rising up from within them, and these young brave women spoke to others, more and more, their voices like waves held back for too long and now rushing towards the shore.

THE END

THE MERMAID

One night as I lay on my bed,
I lay so fast asleep,
When the thought of my true love came running to my
  head,
And poor sailors that sail on the deep.

As I sailed out one day, one day,
And being not far from land,
And there I spied a mermaid a-sitting on a rock,
With a comb and a glass in her hand.

The song she sang, she sang so sweet,
But no answer at all could us make,
Till at length our gallant ship, she tooked round about,
Which made all our poor hearts to ache.

Then up stepped the helmsman of our ship,
In his hand a lead and a line,
All for to sound the seas, my boys, that is so wide and
  deep,
But no hard rock or sand could he find.

Then up stepped the captain of our ship,
And a well-speaking man is he.
He says: 'I have a wife, my boys, in fair Plymouth town,
But this night and a widow she will be.'

Then up stepped the bosun of our ship,
And a well-spoken man was he.
He says: 'I have two sons, my boy, in fair Bristol town,
And orphans I fear they will be.'

And then up stepped the little cabin boy,
And a pretty boy was he.
He says: 'Oh, I grieve for my own mother dear,
Whom I shall nevermore see.'

'Last night when the moon shined bright,
My mother had sons five,
But now she may look in the salt salt seas
And find but one alive.'

Call a boat, call a boat, my fair Plymouth boys,
Don't you hear how the trumpets sound?
For the want of a long-boat in the ocean we were lost,
And the most of our merry men drowned.

Taken from *The Penguin Book of English Folk Songs*, edited by
R. Vaughan Williams and A. L. Lloyd

ACKNOWLEDGEMENTS

Thanks, as ever, to a wonderful group of people who have made writing *The Pearl in the Ice* not just possible, but a delight. I'm lucky to have a wonderful agent, Hilary Delamere, whose wise advice and infectious enthusiasm have been invaluable. My publisher, Barry Cunningham, cheerily stepped in with suggestions and I'm a grateful recipient of his enormous story-making experience. Rachel Leyshon, my glamorous editor, both reassured and pushed for a more cohesive, thoughtful and nuanced text and I'm incredibly lucky to have had her encouragement. Thanks also to Rachel Hickman who took the enormous pile of images I supplied and calmly came up with such an enticing vision for the book. Elinor Bagenal is the best person to set a book free and watch it fly to distant lands. Thanks are also due to Laura for her quiet, determined patience with the final stages of the text as well as Daphne for the rigorous copy-edit. And then the legends: Jazz, Lucy, Esther, Kes and Sarah who make Chicken House a wonderful place to be part of. I'm also grateful to Helen Crawford-White for the dramatic cover design. Thanks also to Nina for her deft hand at pushing a writer who was definitely born to blush unseen. It's been an enchanting journey.

Outside the coop, I'd like to thank Jane Fior who took the time to read *The Pearl in the Ice* along the way and steer me away from choppy waters with wise counsel. And my writing group, Ange, Fatima and Sarah who have kindly commented on my writing for years and years and years.

And then to Charles – thank you, thank you. For the tea, for the support, for our world. (You still owe me a runaway house.) Here's to future fun. Thanks, too, to my glorious roaring boys, M and R, and of course my wondrous, resilient 'little' S. Thanks also to Rhiannon.

This is, very obviously, a work of fiction and so I decided, from the very earliest sketches, to blur the history and write in the spirit, rather than the letter, of the past. But three real people's experience informed the concerns underpinning *The Pearl in the Ice*. The first is that of my grandfather, who served on HMS *Vengeance* at the battle of Jutland in 1916. In thirty-six hours, eight thousand British and German men and twenty-five boats were lost but my grandfather was one of those lucky men who came home. My great-uncle William was not so fortunate. He was twenty years old when he was killed by an exploding shell in Northern France, just one of millions who lost their lives on the death-clogged fields of the First World War. His parents never recovered from the loss of him. Such is the waste of war. A third ghost hovers at the very edge of these pages: my mother. She gave me a most precious gift – infinite love and a language to express it in and as I get older, I become ever more grateful to her. It was also from her cheek that I stole that final, parting, pearl-shaped tear. How she would have loved to have stayed longer.

THE WOLF PRINCESS

On a school trip to Russia, Sophie and her two friends find themselves abandoned on a train. They are rescued by the glamorous Princess Anna Volkonskaya, who takes them to her winter palace and mesmerizes them with stories of lost diamonds and a tragic past.

But as night falls and wolves prowl, Sophie discovers more than dreams in the crumbling palace of secrets . . .

It's got everything I looked for in a book: adventure, mystery, a touch of romance; elements of fairy tale, good triumphing over bad; best friends; a gorgeous horse — and wolves to boot.

BOOKS FOR KEEPS

This story is exciting, heart-warming and totally satisfying. Curl up with Cathryn, jump on that unexpected train and steam through the snow — wolves and a magical palace await you.

LOVEREADING4KIDS

Paperback, ISBN 978-1-910002-09-4, £6.99 • ebook, ISBN 978-1-908435-55-2, £6.99

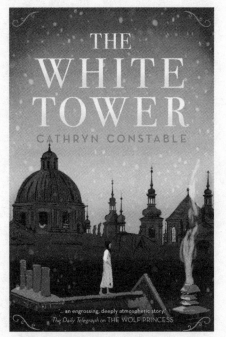

THE WHITE TOWER

Livy's best friend has died. Lost in grief, she wonders if she'll ever feel normal again.

She starts at a new school, Temple College. By day, she struggles to fit in – and by night, she's inexplicably drawn to the roof of the ancient White Tower. Climbing fearlessly among the turrets and stone angels, she has the strangest sensation – of weightlessness, of blood burning in her veins. Up here, somehow, it's as if she might fly.

But others are watching Livy among the Sentinels – others to whom the secret of flight is one they'll do anything to discover.

A delicious mix of contemporary school life, ancient mystery and dreamy magical realism.
THE BOOKSELLER

Paperback, ISBN 978-1-909489-10-3, £6.99 • ebook, ISBN 978-1-910002-08-7, £6.99

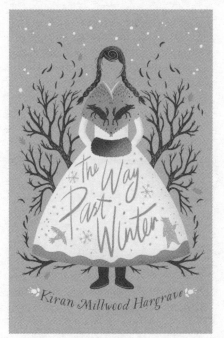

THE WAY PAST WINTER
by KIRAN MILLWOOD HARGRAVE

Mila wakes to find her brother Oskar has vanished. He wouldn't just go and yet a golden clue suggests he's followed a stranger who visited after dark. Then she learns that all the boys in the village have gone . . . except one – the boy-mage called Rune.

Together Mila and Rune set out to find them – in an extraordinary journey across mountains overrun by wolves to the furthest frozen seas of the North.

Kiran is such a beautiful, sparkling writer. This gorgeous story of bravery, sisterhood, goodbyes and beginnings is a must for everyone.
JESSIE BURTON

Paperback, ISBN 978-1-912626-07-6, £6.99 • ebook, 978-1-911490-35-7, £6.99

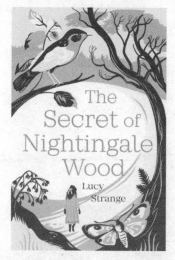

THE SECRET OF NIGHTINGALE WOOD
by LUCY STRANGE

Something terrible has happened in the Abbott family and nobody is talking about it.

Mama is ill. Father has taken a job abroad. Nanny Jane is too busy looking after baby Piglet to pay any attention to Henrietta and the things she sees – or thinks she sees – in the shadows of their new home, Hope House.

All alone, with only stories for company, Henry discovers that Hope House is full of strange secrets: a forgotten attic, thick with cobwebs; ghostly figures glimpsed through dusty windows; mysterious firelight that flickers in the trees beyond the garden.

One night she ventures into the darkness of Nightingale Wood. What she finds there will change her whole world ...

Superbly balanced between readability and poetry [. . .] this is an assured debut.

GUARDIAN

Perfect in so many ways!

EMMA CARROLL

Paperback, ISBN 978-1-910655-03-0, £6.99 • ebook, ISBN 978-1-910655-63-4, £6.99